HOW
HEROES
HEAL

HOW HEROES HEAL

STORIES OF FIRST RESPONDERS AND
THE JOURNEY FROM POSTTRAUMATIC
STRESS INJURY TO POSTTRAUMATIC
GROWTH

MARILYN J. WOOLEY, PHD

HOW HEROES HEAL

Stories of First Responders and the Journey from Posttraumatic Stress Injury to Posttraumatic Growth

Marilyn J. Wooley, PhD

Published by Wild Wooley Publishing
ISBN: 979-8-9865498-0-4

In loving memory of Bill Baxter—"My Angel."

CONTENTS

PREFACE

Unknowingly, I have been acquainted with PTSD for my entire life. It has shaped my perceptions, influenced my relationships, and changed the work I do as a clinician.

As a child, I accepted the PTSD in my family as the normal state of affairs. When I was quite small, I asked my grandfather a question and received a sharp, hurtful retort followed by stony silence. I learned not to ask him questions. I thought it was natural that no one talked about feelings, perceptions, or their lives. I didn't know the reason, but I knew enough not to ask. Still, I wondered. Why had my grandfather slept in a cold windowless room off the basement of my grandparents' beautiful Greek Revival home in Maryland? Why did he remove all the light bulbs in the house at night?

The only emotion I can recall him showing was rage when someone tried to pass him on the road. He would accelerate so fast my small body would slam into the leather of the back seat of his Lincoln Continental. I was curious about the reason my mother was terrified to let my grandfather drive when I was a passenger in his car, but I knew not to ask.

I thought it odd that my friends had conversations with their parents and grandparents and couldn't imagine how that might happen in my family. There was no laughter when my grandfather was around. He was suspicious of practically everyone, including the grocery clerk, the gas station attendant, the Federal Government, the US Army, and me. He obsessed that others would steal from him or betray him. In the midst of my teenage rebellion, I bought a pack of cigarettes from a machine with no intention of smoking. My grandparents found it, unopened, in my things and interrogated me like I had betrayed them and had lost their trust. Given my grandfather's state of mind, I'm pretty sure I never gained it back.

My grandfather was isolated, angry, depressed, and lost. His road rage eventually caused him to flip his car trying to pass a semi-truck on a muddy road. My grandmother sustained a severe head injury in the accident, and never walked or talked again. My grandfather dedicated the rest of his life to caring for her and wore himself out. One day, when my father was visiting, my grandfather apparently felt his heart failing. He sent my father away, arranged his will and other documents on the dining room table, and died alone without asking for help. It wasn't until years later that I realized he suffered from PTSD, which left a legacy for generations.

In the late 1970s, I graduated from the University of Arizona with a PhD in psychology and accepted a post-doctoral internship at Long Beach Veterans Administration Medical Center. My first rotation was on the Acute Spinal Cord Injury ward working with paralyzed Vietnam vets. This was before the *Diagnostic and Statistical Manual* (DSM), the tome mental health professionals used to diagnose patients, listed posttraumatic stress disorder as a diagnosis. The attitude toward veterans with PTSD was definitely not as enlightened as in current times. In fact, soon after my arrival, one of my supervisors informed me that the paralyzed Vietnam vets had "personality problems" before entering the service and that's the reason they had developed post-injury depression, anxiety, and alcoholism. I was young in my career and didn't initially make the connection between these war veterans and my grandfather.

One of the training opportunities, Grand Rounds, was scheduled weekly to present a case history, a clinical interview of a newly admitted patient, and to offer clinicians the opportunity to discuss a differential diagnosis of the patient. One morning I attended Grand Rounds with twenty or so mostly Korean War era psychiatrists. The interviewing psychiatrist was a few years older than I. The hospital patient was a Vietnam-era vet who had served active duty in Southeast Asia in the late 1960s. Before being admitted to the VA Hospital, he'd been found hiding behind his sofa, screaming, and crying, and completely disoriented.

During the interview, he was so distressed he could barely put a sentence together without breaking down. The interviewing psychiatrist managed to pull from the patient that he had been in "reconnaissance" while serving in Vietnam, and at the end of his tour had been "debriefed" to never tell anyone what he had experienced. In gasping sobs, he sputtered that he had been involved in massacres of women and children. He had never told anyone and could not live with the secrets inside himself one moment longer. I sat on the edge of my chair, listening, almost holding my breath. My stomach felt tight, and my heart rate accelerated. I recall thinking, "This is the type of person I want to help."

At the end of the interview, the interviewing psychiatrist asked the rest of the doctors to offer diagnoses.

"He just wants three hots and a cot," one said. Others chimed in: "He's malingering."

"He's clearly psychotic."

"He's delusional."

"He has a personality disorder." "He has alcohol-induced dementia."

Finally, the interviewing psychiatrist asked, "What makes you think he's delusional? Or malingering, or suffering from dementia?"

"Because," one of the observing psychiatrists said, "he's making all that up. None of that ever happened."

In the meantime, I was feeling rather stupid because I'd believed what the patient had said and had been thinking about what kind of treatment he would need. I kept my mouth shut and sat back in my chair.

Then the young psychiatrist said, "Well, in truth, our patient was truthful. The horrors that he witnessed happened just as he described."

"How do you know?" another psychiatrist demanded.

"I was there," the young psychiatrist said. "In Southeast Asia during the war. I saw it all."

His words were a sudden burst of reality. In an instant, I realized that if I truly listened to a person, my gut instinct could lead me to the truth.

I also learned that some professionals are not aware, or hopeful, that patients could be helped in their suffering. Another patient on my ward taught me humility. After I introduced myself to him, he told me, "Don't waste your time on me. I'm walking out of here. In fact, I'm going to walk to a baseball game next spring."

In my wet behind the ears, new clinician smugness, I decided to help this patient overcome his denial that he had a severe spinal cord injury and would never walk again. I repeatedly went to his bedside to engage him. He repeatedly told me there were other guys on the ward who needed me more. I wrote in his chart, "This patient is entrenched in denial." One day, months after I'd left to work on other rotations, I came back to visit the spinal cord injury ward. I was surprised to see this same patient—walking. With a cane and a limp but walking. He wore a baseball T-shirt with the logo of his favorite team. He made a little detour in my direction, gave me a big smile, and winked. Without a word, he walked out of the ward.

My dad's death in 1992, only 14 years after my grandfather, was shrouded with trauma. I inherited several Army issue trunks, but I didn't feel up to opening them for months. When I did open them, I was amazed to find they were full of hundreds of letters, documents, and photographs from my grandfather.

I'd known that my grandfather graduated from West Point, served in WWII, and retired as a Brigadier General, but, because no one ever talked about meaningful things in my family, I was never told the details of his career. I wasn't expecting the rich history I discovered. I was surprised to learn that, at West Point, he'd been known as a jokester with a great sense of humor. A box tied with a ribbon contained the letters he wrote to his mother during his courtship of my grandmother. I laughed until I cried while reading his description of his method for cleverly winning the affections of my grandmother, when it was completely clear she had him at hello.

Digging deeper into a trunk filled with framed family photos, I found a white cardboard jewelry box like one might use to package a pearl necklace. Packaged carefully inside was a white oval frame holding a black and white photo of my grandparents. My grandmother is seated at an ornate vanity table looking up at my grandfather standing beside her. Their images are reflected in the vanity mirror, and they are clearly in love. On the back of the frame, written in my grandmother's hand, I read: "Here is a photo of my handsome George before that horrible war turned his beautiful blond hair all white."

That was my first awareness of what WWII cost my family.

During WWII, my grandfather began his commission in North Africa. His letters from the beginning of deployment were filled with gossip about various commanders with whom he served, an occasional complaint about physical hardships, and advice to my grandmother about shopping wisely to save money. As I kept digging, I discovered photograph albums he'd compiled. As a member of the Signal Corps, my grandfather had taken hundreds of photos of his travels, including towns and cities devastated by the war. There were more sinister photos to come at the bottom of the trunk.

In 1945, he had been among the liberators of Dachau Concentration Camp. The scenes in the photos, now familiar to the world, were horrific. I tried to imagine how he must have felt walking in the camp with little or no awareness of what the Allied troops would find. He wrote to my grandmother describing blood running in the trenches, bodies stacked like cordwood, and the 50 boxcars of bodies that they "didn't get to in time." He befriended a priest who survived the war by making bricks for the crematoriums. He seemed fascinated by this priest, and I imagined he must have wondered how he would have or could have survived in similar circumstances. One of the photos was taken during the arrest of Hermann Goering. Sitting next to Goering was my grandfather as one of the arresting officers.

The letters following the trip to Dachau became increasingly angry, even enraged. He wanted to be transferred to the Pacific. He complained about the post-war conditions. He seemed to become increasingly hostile and isolated. The letters he wrote after the war, when he was safely living with my grandmother in Maryland, seemed to portray his increasing isolation and suspiciousness. He complained about everything from his pay scale to the health care he received at Walter Reed to the stupidity of his peers. He seemed to feel abandoned and betrayed by the United States after all he had endured to serve the country he had loved.

The experience of looking through the trunks overwhelmed me. I could not wrap my mind around what I'd seen and read and put everything back in the trunk. Months later, I traveled to the East Coast to attend a training conference on the diagnosis and treatment of PTSD. While there, I visited the Holocaust Museum in Washington, DC. I recall taking a "passport" of an individual who had been imprisoned and getting into an elevator that resembled a gas chamber. The elevator rose to the fourth floor and the doors opened. As we exited, we were confronted by a life-size photo on the wall of the Allied GIs looking at us. Most had a shocked "thousand-yard stare" into the distance. Suddenly, everything that I'd learned about my grandfather struck me to the core. I comprehended the horrors he confronted and went through the museum as if witnessing the death camp through his eyes. I found myself thinking I should be crying, but I couldn't. I was numb and a little dissociated and confused about how my grandfather went from a confident, well-liked, good-humored individual to the isolated, fearful, angry man I knew as a child.

When I returned to the conference, a WWII fighter pilot veteran named Quentin Aanenson presented a touching video titled, "A Fighter Pilot's Story" about his war experiences. After Mr. Aanenson's presentation, I spoke to him in the hopes he could explain how the war affected my grandfather. I asked, "Why did Dachau change him so much? What kept him from talking about it? Why didn't anyone ever tell me what he experienced?"

Mr. Aanenson said simply, "Don't you see? He felt guilty."

"Guilty?" I asked. "But he helped liberate the prisoners. He saved their lives. He helped arrest Hermann Goering."

"Yes, guilty," Mr. Aanenson replied. "He felt guilty because he was afraid."

And then I understood that my grandfather's unresolved PTSD had not only stolen my grandfather's personality, but it had also robbed him of his hope for the future, trust in humanity, and even his soul. I also knew that my calling was to help prevent others exposed to repeated trauma from suffering a similar fate.

SECTION 1

THE BASICS

This section provides the basic explanation of concepts that will be referred to in subsequent chapters that include the stories of the first responders.

DOC, AM I GOING CRAZY?

Unless you have experienced PTSD yourself, it's difficult to understand how bizarre it feels and how impossible it is to describe it logically. It's like you are locked in fear. Your body unpredictably reacts to a threat that's not there. The thinking part of your brain might tell you that you are perfectly safe, but your body reacts as if a threat is imminent. You become irritable and angry at the smallest provocation. Being around others becomes a chore. Distressing images and overwhelming physical sensations hijack your will and may lead to an extreme and terrifying manifestation of PTSD—a flashback.

Three years on the job, police officer Mark had responded to a horrific robbery-gone-wrong of a small, family-owned Chinese take-out restaurant. He was the first on scene and walked into a slaughter. All five members of the family who owned the restaurant had been shot multiple times. One young woman had tried to run and was killed in the cooler. Blood covered the walls, floors, and countertops. The strong smell of Chinese spices and cooking oil intermingled with the smell of death and Mark's own fear. His senses were completely overwhelmed.

I met Mark months later. As part of the forensic investigation, he'd rehearsed what he'd witnessed and described the fear he experienced so many times that he could speak about it in a rote, superficially coherent manner. Nonetheless, the pieces continued to fragment in his mind and the gruesome vision haunted his dreams. Even when he was awake, the vision of the terror on dead victims' faces could appear randomly directly in front of his eyes.

Mark's worst flashback occurred during a therapy session. The smell of Chinese food wafted from a nearby kitchen. Suddenly Mark lost all sense of presence and was transported back to the scene of the murders.

The vision of blood and the smell of slaughter surrounded him. He fell on the floor shouting and trying to take cover. His reaction to the trigger was so powerful that he literally perceived that he was back in the scene. When he finally came back to the present, he was embarrassed and apologetic. He said, "Doc, I must be going crazy."

DEFINITIONS

WHAT IS A CRISIS?

A crisis is an acute emotional reaction to some powerful stimulus or a demand. A crisis can lead to disruption to a person's state of psychological balance; the failure of usual coping mechanisms; distress; impairment, or dysfunction.

WHAT IS TRAUMA?

Trauma is a horrific event outside of the realm of usual human experience. The person experiencing it finds it markedly distressing and feels fear, helplessness, and horror. After trauma, people begin to form a membrane around themselves that insulates them from additional trauma.

Trauma can happen to anyone. There are no boundaries regarding age, gender, socioeconomic status, race, ethnicity, or sexual orientation. According to the National Center for PTSD (2021), 60% of men and 50% of women will experience a traumatic event in their lives. In the US, 7% to 8% of the population will develop PTSD during their lifetimes from rape or sexual abuse, traffic accidents, witnessing violent crime, and so on. Children who grow up in violent families may also develop PTSD.

First responders are exposed to extremely stressful and traumatic events, including death, serious injury, disasters, and putting their personal safety at risk on a regular basis. One of my clients, an EMT with thirty years on the job, estimated that he had witnessed a minimum of 46,000 critical events over the course of his career. He didn't consider the impact they had on him at the time they occurred because "they were just part of the job." There is a definite cost, however. Lewis-Schroeder et al. (2018) reported that evidence suggests that the prevalence of PTSD is substantially higher among first responders than in the general population. For example, Tull (2020) notes that 7% to 37% of firefighters meet the diagnostic criteria for PTSD, and Badge of Life (2016) estimated that 150,000 police officers in the US have symptoms of PTSD.

WHAT ARE CRITICAL INCIDENTS?

Critical incidents are abrupt, powerful events that fall outside the range of ordinary human experiences and can be defined as any event that has a stressful impact sufficient to overwhelm the usually effective coping skills of an individual. Jeff Mitchell and George Everly (2001), founders of the International Critical Incident Stress Foundation, define a critical incident as, "Any situation faced by emergency service personnel that causes them to experience unusually strong emotional reactions, which have the potential to interfere with their ability to function at the scene or later." Roger Soloman (2011) offers another description: "Any situation beyond the realm of a person's usual experience that overwhelms his or her sense of vulnerability and/or lack of control over the situation."

WHAT IS CRITICAL INCIDENT STRESS?

Critical incident stress (CIS), also called posttraumatic stress, is an acute emotional, cognitive, and physical *reaction* that results from an exposure to a powerful, horrible, terrifying, threatening, or grotesque stimulus to an overwhelming demand or circumstance. Critical incident stress is a normal response in normal, healthy people to a terribly abnormal event that often overwhelms coping mechanisms. Critical incident stress is normal after trauma but becomes dangerous to health when it's not resolved (Mitchell & Everly, 2001). Critical incident trauma occurs when the result of a perceived, life-threatening, event exceeds one's ability to cope.

WHAT IS CUMULATIVE STRESS?

Stress is a routine part of daily life. Eustress for example is a positive and can motivate you to finish a project, ask your boss for a raise, or run a marathon. On the other hand, cumulative stress comes from day-to-day mental, emotional, or physical strain resulting from adverse or highly demanding circumstances. Cumulative stress is unmitigated stress arousal that builds over time.

Ultimately, cumulative stress can lead to physical, mental, or behavioral symptoms, including headaches, stomachaches, irritability, insomnia, and other medical and psychological conditions. First responders are particularly vulnerable to cumulative stress because every day they are exposed to events that reveal the harshest sides of humanity. Cumulative stress builds over a career and can be just as disabling as critical incident or traumatic stress. Worse, cumulative stress is insidious and often undiagnosed because it isn't associated with one event.

Cumulative stress. Three identifiable phases include:

a) Stress arousal
b) Energy conservation, such as isolating or not partaking in usual activities
c) Exhaustion

By the time the person is exhausted, they are often in need of outside intervention, including psychotherapy.

WHAT IS PTSD?

PTSD is an injury that causes dysfunction to parts of the brain. PTSD can result from both cumulative and critical incident or traumatic stress. Symptoms include reliving events, avoiding situations that remind the person of the events, feeling constantly keyed up (hyperarousal), and the development of negative feelings about oneself. PTSD can lead to depression, extreme anxiety, distress, and deadening of the senses to the point an individual doesn't feel fully alive. Emotional numbing keeps a person from being able to feel love or connection to family members. The visceral physical feelings induced by strong emotions can be unbearable and lead to maladaptive, dysfunctional, or antisocial patterns of behavior. In some cases, frantic attempts to escape the pain may lead to isolation, self-harm, or even suicide attempts. Less obvious but more insidious are the epidemically high rates of stress-related cardiovascular disease, divorce, and addiction.

PTSD symptoms:

- Behavioral signs include agitation, irritability, hostility, hypervigilance, self-destructive behavior, or social isolation.
- Psychological symptoms include flashbacks, fear, severe anxiety, or mistrust.
- Mood changes include loss of interest or pleasure in activities, guilt, or loneliness.
- Sleep disturbances can include insomnia or nightmares.
- Other symptoms may include emotional detachment or unwanted thoughts.

POSTTRAUMATIC STRESS DISORDER VS. POSTTRAUMATIC STRESS INJURY

Posttraumatic stress injury (PTSI) refers to the same set of symptoms as posttraumatic stress disorder (PTSD). The difference is the conceptualization of what caused the symptoms. Whereas PTSD refers to a mental disorder, PTSI refers to a biological injury or trauma. A mental disorder, also called a mental illness, causes distress or impairment in personal functioning, and is associated with significant stigma. An injury, on the other hand, refers to damage caused to the body, in the case of PTSI the brain, by an external force and is generally considered less frightening and disabling. Researchers have established the physical changes that happen in the nervous system with PTSD and mental health experts understand and acknowledged those changes. Some argue that changing the name from PTSD to PTSI would also change people's perception of the condition (Foskett, 2020).

I often tell my clients they "sprained their brain" to explain their symptoms, which after all were created secondary to an event that happened to them, not something they randomly developed. This seems less confusing and more hopeful than telling them they have a disorder. Although PTSD is still the most used term and therefore will be utilized throughout this book, I support the adoption of PTSI to help reduce the stigma of this condition.

CRITICAL INCIDENTS

The most significant critical incidents experienced by first responders are listed below.

1. **Line-of-duty death (LODD).** As I'm writing this, an officer who was visiting the National Law Enforcement Officers Memorial in Washington, DC, texted me and sent a photo of the engraving of the name of a fallen law enforcement officer we both knew. He wrote, "I was astounded by the emotion I felt to see all those names." Over twenty-one thousand names of officers are engraved on that wall.

   Any first responder who is placed in harm's way might be killed in the line of duty. Law enforcement officers may be killed by gunfire, in auto accidents, or from medical reasons such as a stress-related heart attack or stroke. Disturbingly, in 2021, the number of law enforcement officers feloniously killed was 73—the highest in 20 years excluding the terrorist attacks in 2001 (Tucker, E., & Krishnakumar, 2022).

   Firefighters die in burnovers or rapidly progressing fires, vehicle accidents, falls, or from exposure to hazards. Causes of death include sudden cardiac death, stroke, internal trauma and crushing, and smoke inhalation/asphyxia (Fahy, R., Petrillo, J. T., & Molis, J. L. 2020).

In any case, a LODD is not only distressing because of the loss of the colleague, but because it forces those left behind to face their own vulnerability during the performance of their jobs.

Leo, a firefighter, survived a terrifying fire tornado and heard his friend's May Day call seconds before his death. His story is told in Chapter 1.

2. **Suicide of colleague.** The ultimate tragedy of unresolved trauma in first responders may be the act of suicide. First responders are thought to be more resilient than the general population. However, exposure to critical incidents, the development of posttraumatic stress, and the resultant emotional decompensation and social isolation, can make them susceptible to self-harm, or even suicide. A high rate of suicide continues to plague first responders, especially law enforcement. Law enforcement is one of the most toxic careers in the world and has been compared to being in a war zone.

According to Blue H.E.L.P. (2021), a nonprofit dedicated to acknowledging "the service and sacrifice of law enforcement officers we lost to suicide," the number of deaths attributed to suicide has recently increased. Data reveals that in 2017, 168 law enforcement officers died of suicide, followed by 172 in 2018, and 228 in 2019. These numbers exceed the number of line-of-duty deaths in those same years making suicide the top officer safety issue. According to Spence and Drake (2021), a U.S. Department of Justice report expressed that the U.S. Congress is "disturbed by increased reports of suicide by current and former law enforcement officers."

In fact, the overall rate of suicide in first responders, in general, exceeds the rate in the general public. A survey of more than 4,000 first responders found that 6.6% had attempted suicide, which is more than 10 times the rate in the general population (Venteicher, 2017). Additionally, because of the stigma associated with suicide, the numbers are likely underreported (Tiesman et al, 2021). Unfortunately, despite increasing knowledge on how to successfully treat PTSD and related disorders, this rate has not seemed to decrease. Furthermore, the stigma of suicide precludes the death from being considered a line of duty death, so honors and benefits, such as death benefits and health insurance for surviving family members are excluded. Legislation is being proposed to change the suicide exclusion by redefining PTSD as a presumptive injury (Orrick, D., 2022).

Finally, the suicide of a colleague is devastating to first responders who may blame themselves for not being able to prevent it, and thus become traumatized themselves.

Dillon in Chapter 2 was a cop's cop until a supervisor committed suicide. The incident haunted Dillon for the rest of his career and nearly devastated his life.

3. **Officer involved shootings (OIS)** are defined as the intentional or accidental discharge of a firearm by a police officer. Not only can the potential consequences be life changing, but the subsequent administrative and legal proceedings surrounding the investigation of the OIS, which can take weeks to months, can result in ongoing significant anxiety to both the officers and their families.

Killing or witnessing injury or death of an innocent person, for example, shooting a civilian caught in the line of fire, may be even more devasting and can lead to moral injury, the intense guilt, shame, and spiritual crisis which can develop when one violates their own moral code. Many departments have realized the psychological impact of post-shooting trauma and now require an interview with a psychologist post OIS to mitigate the effects.

Two officer involved shootings are discussed in this book.

Sonny, a cop on the gang task force, got into a shootout with a gang member who threatened to kill Sonny's partner. Inadvertently, his gunfire killed a young woman who Sonny had not seen in the line of fire. He describes the aftermath in Chapter 5.

Bobby expected to have a quiet morning cup of coffee until a child killer ruined his day and almost his life. His story is in Chapter 9.

4. **Serious line-of-duty injury** includes being shot by a suspect, hit by a car, trapped in a burnover, smoke inhalation, and other causes. In addition to the shock of the injury, the recovery process is often long and arduous, and the responder's family may be significantly affected.

Highway Patrol Officer Fred had been an adrenaline junkie since middle school. Aside from his time in the marines, serving as a patrolman was the best thing he'd ever done. One rainy, moonless night, he was on duty riding shotgun with another officer. They were patrolling along a remote two-lane highway. An SUV passed them headed in the opposite direction traveling at least 25 mph over the speed limit. Fred's partner began a U-turn to pursue the SUV. Out of the dark, a truck with no headlights on appeared and T-boned the patrol vehicle on Fred's side. Fred was knocked unconscious.

He awoke as he was being loaded into an ambulance on the way to the emergency room. He'd sustained a concussion, two cracked ribs, a broken arm, and damage to his lumbar spine. After his injuries healed to some degree with the help of physical therapy, he tried to return to patrol. However, within months, his back began aching so much that he could barely tolerate wearing his service belt. He started burning his vacation days when he couldn't make it to work. He fought with workers' comp to get an appointment with a neurologist. His commander began harassing him about his performance. The pain and stress started to get to him. He became more irritable. He and his wife began to fight. Finally, the neurologist diagnosed him with a spinal problem that needed surgery. "Too bad we didn't catch this earlier," the doctor told him. After surgery, the pain didn't abate as he had hoped. He spent another six months fighting the pain before he realized he was never going back to work. He had two young sons and retirement at his age was not in his plans. "Two seconds was all it took to ruin my life," he said. He's still working through it.

Max, a firefighter, barely survived a helicopter crash. He tells of his physical, emotional, and spiritual recovery in Chapter 3.

5. **Disasters/Multi-casualty incidents/Catastrophes** include: 9/11, the Murrow Building in Oklahoma City, multiple auto collisions, multiple homicides, and multi-fatality fires. No matter how prepared first responders are, no matter how much training the department has offered, few are completely ready for the chaos of a large-scale incident. Many experience frustration and hopelessness when the scene is chaotic, and their skills are not utilized to the fullest. They often are left with the perception they could have done more.

   Victor, a wildland firefighter, witnessed a helicopter filled with his work friends explode in midair and crash into a mountain. After the horror, he began to blame himself and his life spiraled downward. He recounts his struggle to redeem himself in Chapter 4.

6. **Significant events involving children** affect almost everyone. Children are innocent and vulnerable. They need protection. Harm to a child is especially devastating when the responder believes that the incident could have been prevented, or even worse, that they could have acted faster or more competently.

   Willa responded to the homicide of children she knew well. She was left with the perception that had she been able to predict the future she could have done more and prevented the deaths. Her story is told in Chapter 6.

7. **Events in which the victim is known to the personnel** are likely in rural areas where community members have close contact. To arrive at a scene with known victims can be one of the most stressful incidents a first responder can encounter.

   Sam, a police officer in a rural medium-sized town recalled, "There are so many calls where I've known the victim. I've responded to a fellow officer's suicide, a SIDS death in the home of close friend, and a friend in my department had to shoot and kill the drug enraged son of a Sergeant who worked in a neighboring department, and so on. I've lost count of them all."

* * *

Tom served as an officer in a small mountain town. He worked on patrol and served as the school resource officer. One of the duties that gave him the most gratification was teaching the high school driving safety program. One afternoon, he left class to begin patrol. Within minutes, dispatch directed him to a vehicle accident on a winding mountain road. He responded, and with horror, realized two of his students had taken a curve too fast and drove off the mountain to their deaths. His duties included investigating the crash but also delivering the death notification to the parents. Suddenly, his primary purpose in life became his greatest burden.

Other incidents in which the responder knew the victim include Leo (Chapter 1), Dillon (Chapter 2), Max (Chapter 3), and Willa (Chapter 6).

8. **Prolonged incidents, especially with the loss of life** may include protracted rescue, or an incident in which response time is extended. Sometimes first responders under stress experience a sense of altered time that affects their perception of the event and gives it special meaning.

   Larry had served with a small police department for five years. Late one night, dispatch put out a call for a loud party in a rural neighborhood. Larry and his partner responded. The party was loud and boisterous, and attended by a few dozen underage teens, mostly intoxicated. At the sight of Larry and his partner, a small riot ensued. Larry called for backup, but the response time in that part of the county was at least 30 minutes.

Suddenly, the sound of gunshots burst from a swale in the side yard. Someone was shooting at the officers. A girl from the house began screaming, "Dad! Dad! No! Don't!" Larry began to return fire and squeezed the trigger just as the girl ran directly in front of him. Fortunately, he didn't fire. Floodlights unexpectedly illuminated the entire yard. Larry stood in his dark uniform against a white shed wall with bullets from the suspect rushing past his head. Momentarily he froze. His partner aimed at the suspect and shot him, fatally. Time slowed. In Larry's mind, the incident took many minutes, when in fact it took a few seconds.

Just as the suspect was neutralized, the daughter ran screaming into the swale and flung herself on her father's body. Her screams reverberated in Larry's head. Time dragged on while he waited for relief officers, the medics, and the coroner to arrive. The sights and sounds of the incident stayed lodged in the front of Larry's mind for a very long time. When I met him months later, he was blaming himself for freezing in fear and had become convinced that his personal actions were the cause of the suspect's death and the girl's distress. In fact, at the mere recollection of the incident, Larry threw up in my garbage can. He eventually decided to leave his law enforcement career and found happiness in a different type of job.

Francine, the 9-1-1 dispatcher, experienced two prolonged incidents that left her with grave self-doubt. She tells her story in Chapter 7.

9. **Personally threatening situations** occur when the first responder feels that their own life is in danger whether from an armed suspect or in a fire, vehicle crash, or building collapse.

Hank was patrolling alone in a remote mountainous area late at night and stopped to assist what he thought was a stranded motorist. The motorist turned out to be a psychiatric patient who assaulted Hank with a machete, nearly severing his arm. Bleeding profusely, Hank escaped the assailant and struggled back to his car. He had no radio or cell contact, and even so, backup was more than an hour away. He was saved by a local resident who heard him yelling and called the home of an off-duty peace officer to assist. The off-duty officer had just returned home. He responded to the scene and managed to neutralize the assailant before he could attend to Hank's severe wounds.

Dillon, whom we will meet in Chapter 2, tells of another incident in which he was nearly killed, and a close friend died. Then he had a frightening encounter with a colleague that made him feel unsafe in his own agency. We meet him again in Chapter 8.

10. **Events with extensive or excessive media interest** are common, especially in high-profile cases when the first responders may feel most vulnerable.

Robert O'Donnell, the firefighter who in 1987 pulled 18-month-old Baby Jessica from a well after a protracted 58-hour rescue attempt that received one of the highest television ratings, committed suicide seven years later. Apparently, once the media disappeared after his 15 minutes of fame, he could never return to his normal life. The father of two committed suicide four days after the Oklahoma City bombing (Katz, 1995).

Other incidents in which excessive media interest played a part include Victor (Chapter 4) and Bobby (Chapter 9).

11. **Extremely personal incidents and cumulative stress** make first responders more vulnerable to posttraumatic stress. First responders typically encounter hundreds if not thousands of events during their careers. Because they are resilient, they may not develop symptoms unless an incident is especially personal to them, or they have reached a point where they feel completely overloaded.

Thad is a firefighter with a small-town fire department. It's not uncommon for him to respond to calls involving people he knows. The incident that put him over the edge was a house fire in his neighborhood. The home belonged to an elderly woman, about the same age as his grandparents.

Some background: Thad was born into a less than functional family and developed early issues trusting people. In grade school, he went to live with his grandparents, whom he adores. To this day, he's always lending a hand with their property, chopping wood, grocery shopping, transporting them to doctor visits, what have you. So, watching out for the old woman was second nature, just like he helped his grandparents.

On the day of the house fire, there was some confusion about which department was to respond and the call came to Thad's station late. By the time his engine arrived at the woman's house, it was fully engulfed. Thad's first impulse was to run into the flames to rescue the woman. He felt rage when his captain ordered him to stand down. Once the fire was out, he rushed into the house and tripped over the woman's charred remains. The image was emblazoned in his mind. His guilt for not disobeying orders and going into the house became overwhelming. He was angry with his captain, himself, the world. Until he got treatment, going back to work was out of the question.

Harriett was a tough cop and a sex crimes investigator until she ran into the case that triggered her memories of sexual abuse. Her story is told in Chapter 10.

12. **Administrative abandonment or betrayal** is a form of organizational stress that occurs when a first responder feels abandoned or betrayed by command staff, the agency, or the community after an incident. The consequences of this type of situation can be devastating. First responders refer to their agency and the people they work with as their "family." In that respect, the agency represents the "parental"

figure—the people who are supposed to care about their welfare and provide support and protection in crisis. When the first responder loses faith that his "family" will be there, morale is shattered leading to depression and anger. They take it personally. As trust deteriorates, careers are commonly lost.

Dan and his partner were called to a mobile home park where an armed man was shooting at people. The scene was chaotic. The officers didn't have time to calm the panicked residents and get them to safety before they set out to chase the shooter through a maze of mobile homes. Dan remembers feeling conflicted between helping the residents and finding the shooter.

At one point, Dan lost radio contact with his partner and assumed the worst—that he'd been wounded or killed. Dan continued to search for the shooter. He saw him emerging from the trees and tried to TASER him, but the man kept coming, pointing his rifle at Dan. Dan shot him in the chest three times. The suspect didn't go down. Suddenly, Dan realized that the shooter was wearing a bulletproof vest. As the shooter took aim, Dan took a head shot and neutralized the threat. He felt overwhelming relief finding his partner unharmed. After the scene was cleared and the incident investigators interviewed Dan and his partner, the officers went home, shaken, and sad that a man had to die that day, but glad to have prevented harm to the civilians, and to be alive for their families.

The next day, Dan's captain called him into the office. He said that the shooter's family was upset that Dan killed him with a headshot. Dan explained that there was no other option. The captain ordered Dan to write a letter of apology because he feared that the family would file a lawsuit. Dan was stunned. After he expressed his disbelief in a few choice words, he took off his gun belt and badge, dumped them on the captain's desk, and walked off. Dan made the mistake of thinking that his captain would have his back after this distressing incident. He was wrong.

The episode was so devastating that he never returned to work at that department.

Systemic betrayal can occur when an injured first responder becomes involved in the workers' compensation system. For example, police officers' claims for compensation and psychiatric treatment for PTSD are met with skepticism, resistance, and lengthy delays. Insurance companies can impede injured police officers' recovery by prolonging the claims process with unjustified delays and failing to act on psychiatrist recommendations, even when the claimant was clearly suicidal (Skeffington, 2016). For this reason, I say with some irony that I start treating a first responder for PTSD and soon find I'm treating them for the trauma caused by filing an insurance claim to collect benefits for their traumatic injury.

Willa, whom we will meet in Chapter 6, also experienced administrative abandonment and betrayal as did Victor (Chapter 4).

13. **Multiple critical incidents: Some events are so powerful and overwhelming that multiple critical incidents must be considered.** The January 6, 2021, attack on the US Capitol is an example of a prolonged event that included a number of critical incidents.

At the time of this writing, public opinion varies regarding the events that occurred on January 6, 2021. What is certain is that Capitol police were confronted with a horrific event beyond anything they'd ever experienced. According to court testimony, the officers were outnumbered 50 to 1 by the rioters. Testimony indicated they were physically beaten, tortured, and taunted with racial epithets. They thought they would die trying to defend the Capitol (Wolfe, J., 2021) and fatally wounded a rioter who breached the building. Court testimony reveals that they felt not only overwhelmed by the extended attack, but they also suffered terror, humiliation, helplessness, intense fear for their own personal safety and lives, a lack of backup, and indifference to their suffering. They came to the realization that some of the very people they were trying to defend and protect criticized and abandoned them. The media attention and public scrutiny became yet another level of critical incident stress and potentially magnified perceptions of betrayal and shame. Hours after the riot, Officer Brian Sicknick died from a stroke. Tragically, four of the responding officers committed suicide weeks to months after the riot (Cameron, 2022).

The January 6 Capitol riot exemplified a number of critical incidents, including LODD, suicides of colleagues, OIS, extensive media coverage, extremely personal events (including being called racial epithets), threats to personal safety, a prolonged event with a negative outcome, serious injuries to multiple colleagues, and perceptions of abandonment and betrayal by the community,

Any critical incident can test the resilience of first responders, but the emotional sum of the events surrounding January 6, 2021, has been more than some have been able to endure. Perhaps no one will know all the reasons Officers Gunther Hashide, Kyle DeFreytag, Howard Liebengood, and Jeffrey Smith took their lives, but layers of critical incidents undoubtedly played a role. The fallout will reverberate for years.

A BRIEF TOUR OF THE PSYCHOPHYSIOLOGY OF STRESS

The human brain is remarkable. Its primary function is to keep us alive. Even when people are frustrated or angry about their symptoms, I tell them, "Be patient. It's doing its job the best it can." Psychological problems occur when the internal structures aren't communicating well, when the signals between parts aren't jiving.

The human brain consists of three separate, but interdependent parts, built from the bottom up. The most primitive structure is called the reptilian brain because it contains the ancient structures found in the brains of reptiles beginning about 500 million years ago. It includes the cerebellum and the brainstem, which connects to the spinal column. The reptilian brain controls the body's basic functions. It is ready to go when we are born and takes care of all the things babies need to do to survive, such as regulating body temperature, heart rate, eating, sleeping and waking, feeling pain, urinating and defecating, and balance. The brain stem and its cohort, the hypothalamus, also control the endocrine system and the immune system. In other words, this part of the brain is essential to keeping us alive.

The limbic system emerged in mammals about 150 million years ago. The limbic system lies right above the reptilian brain and is also known as the mammalian brain. Its development occurs after a baby is born, and its job is to regulate emotions, monitor danger, and in general be the command post for value judgments that we make, often unconsciously, that exert a strong influence on our behavior.

The reptilian brain and mammalian brain together make up the "emotional brain." Job duties of the emotional brain include looking out for our welfare, detecting danger, and alerting us to potential opportunities. These structures work together to guide us toward what is helpful for our survival and away from harm by releasing hormones and causing visceral sensations that get our attention and move us in another direction. The emotional brain helps us cope with the challenges of living.

The neocortex appeared in primates two or three million years ago and expanded to take up about 30% of the human brain. The two hemispheres of the human neocortex, or rational brain, have been responsible for human language, abstract thought, consciousness, imagination, and our incredible ability to learn and adapt. The rational brain pays attention to how the people and things in our world operate, how to accomplish our goals, and generally understands consequences so we may make choices about our lives. A well-functioning prefrontal cortex is also associated with the development of empathy, which helps us understand that other people feel and think differently than we do, and hence is essential for getting along well with others.

Language is fundamental for human relationships, and the foundation of the astonishing diversity of human cultures. Ponder for example how the specific language used by first responders is different from that of the general public. First responders not only have vocabulary specific to what they do, but also culturally cope with horrible incidents using dark humor, much of which the public would find offensive or unfeeling.

FEAR

Perceptions and emotions are not located in any specific part of the brain, but rather depend on interconnected areas, or systems, of the brain. Each function has unique pathways between several regions of the brain.

The thalamus is a gatekeeper for all incoming sensory information from the eyes, ears, touch, and kinesthetic senses, aside from smell. It receives and re-routes information to the appropriate sensory cortex, which assigns it meaning. If the cortex doesn't sense a threat, life goes on as usual. However, if there is a perceived threat, the cortex sends the information to a structure called the amygdala, which rapidly produces emotional responses. If the threat is overwhelming, the thalamus may not filter all the information at the same time, leading to sensory overload. People with PTSD often remember the traumatic event as a series of isolated, disjointed sensations and cannot describe it coherently.

The amygdala is an almond-shaped structure located in the limbic system in the emotional brain. The amygdala's function is to help us feel emotions and perceive them in others. The amygdala modulates all our reactions to events that are important to our survival and instinctively leads to the release of stress hormones like cortisol and adrenaline that flood the system in preparation for fight or flight.

But wait! The connections running from our emotional brain to the cortex, our center of conscious control, are far more numerous that the connections running from the cortex down to the emotional brain. Think of the heavy traffic noise on a six-lane interstate highway compared to the comparatively quiet frontage road alongside it. If the perception of danger must go through the thalamus, to the cortex, and back down to the amygdala, time's a-wasting. Fractions of a second have passed and you have not reacted to the threat, which could turn out very badly for you.

Fortunately, there's also a shorter and faster route that bypasses the sensory cortex. In fact, this path is so much faster you may not be consciously aware of the threat until milliseconds later. I reviewed a tape of a police officer confronting an armed suspect. The officer literally drew his weapon at least a second before he was consciously aware of the threat.

Those milliseconds saved by the faster route may save your life, but at a cost. The information received directly by the amygdala is not fine-tuned. The cortex provides more accurate information and relevant details about the nature of the threat a few fractions of a second later. This allows for a rational response to a threat. Think about the consequences of reacting to a suspect who pulls out a drivers' license or a cell phone, but your speedy amygdala reacts as if it were a gun.

The amygdala is a brain structure that recognizes a threat stimulus through implicit memory, an automatic type of memory that accesses memories yet doesn't require a conscious process. When the amygdala receives cues that have been previously associated with danger, signals are sent to the hypothalamus that in turn activate the sympathetic nervous system and adrenal glands.

The hippocampus stores and retrieves explicit memories, that is, conscious memories about the time and place an incident occurred, whom you were with, and so on. Given that it stores the memory of events as well as associated emotional states, it's highly sensitive to aversive events and the context that surrounds them. It not only encodes information about a specific danger, but also generalizes that information in a multitude of ways that can lead to conditioned fear to stimuli that are similar to the original fear-producing situation or object.

When a person undergoes a traumatic experience, both the amygdala and the hippocampus are activated by the same memories, yet the implicit memory of the amygdala and the explicit memory of the hippocampus record different aspects of the event.

For example, the pathway from the amygdala to the cortex is not fully developed in children, nor is the hippocampus or cortex which explains why children cannot explicitly remember very early childhood traumas. Although the amygdala records unconscious memories and traumas experienced by the young child, the immature hippocampus is not developed enough to make sense of those memories. Children can react to early childhood traumas, yet not be able to consciously access those memories in the same way as a mature adult. Years later, the early memories of emotion and sensation associated with trauma can be intensely distressing and disturbing—yet without the awareness that comes with a conscious memory, the adult experiences unbearable physical and emotional pain without any idea of the reason.

Darlene came to me for treatment of severe anxiety, including fear of having sex with her husband. She had been in therapy for some months with another therapist, but she was making little progress. We began actively processing her physical reactions with a technique developed for treating trauma by psychologist Francine Shapiro called Eye Movement Desensitization Reprocessing (EMDR.) One afternoon, she left an intense therapy session still feeling somewhat discouraged because she could not express the source of her anxiety "in words." About 45 minutes later I received a frantic call from her. She could barely speak and was clearly highly distressed. I asked her to come back to my office, thinking I may have to hospitalize her. When she arrived, she was sweating, sobbing, and violently shaking. She told me that while she was driving home, a police car passed her. Suddenly, she lost control of her car and ran off the road. As luck would have it, there was a wide shoulder, and she was able to stop before crashing. She felt safe in my office and eventually calmed down, but again could not verbalize the source of her anxiety and fear, and she had no idea why she was triggered by the police car.

Sensing she suffered trauma as a young child, I asked her if I could speak with her mother. I explained what had happened in and after Darlene's session and inquired if there was some early trauma Darlene had experienced that could have accounted for her symptoms. Darlene's mother began telling a story that she had never revealed to anyone.

When Darlene was a small child, her mother was single and had to rely on daycare to watch Darlene when she went to work. When Darlene was less than two years old, the neighbor, who was married to a police officer, offered to babysit. Darlene's mother felt fortunate to find a nearby sitter who could keep her daughter safe.

After a few months, she became concerned when Darlene became upset and clingy every time she went to the sitter. She finally asked the neighbor if anything had happened to Darlene and was not completely satisfied with the answer. Soon after, she came home early and walked into the sitter's home unannounced. She was horrified at what she saw. The police officer was home alone with Darlene. He was sitting naked on the living room floor with an erect penis, using his service weapon to rape Darlene's tiny vagina. Darlene's mother managed to grab her baby and escape the house. She called law enforcement and the officer was arrested and tried, and eventually sentenced to prison. A physical exam of Darlene revealed physical damage to her vagina and anus. Darlene's mother never discussed the situation with Darlene because she believed she was too young to remember it. That was not entirely true. Darlene's immature hippocampus could not form an explicit memory of the trauma, but her amygdala certainly remembered the terror and physical pain she endured. Fortunately, once the source of her trauma was revealed, Darlene was able to work through it successfully with the use of EMDR and CBT (cognitive behavioral therapy).

DOES PTSD CHANGE YOUR BRAIN?

In a word, the answer is yes. Neuroimaging studies on the brains of people with PTSD show structural changes in the amygdala, hippocampus, the ventromedial prefrontal cortex, and Broca's Area, one of the speech centers of the brain.

When the brain perceives a threat, the adrenal glands flood the body with adrenaline and cortisol. Cortisol works with adrenalin to create memories of short-term emotional events and may serve as a means to remember what to avoid in the future. However, long-term exposure to cortisol damages cells in the hippocampus—the region of the brain that controls learning and short-term memory—results in impaired learning and reduced ability to retrieve already stored information. If the brain becomes trained over time to maintain its fight-or-flight response, leading to continual states of hyper-arousal, permanent neurological changes may occur. Research has shown that people with PTSD, including combat veterans and children reared in abusive families, may have a smaller hippocampus than people without PTSD, meaning they may have trouble discriminating between relevant and nonrelevant environmental stimuli. Thus, people with PTSD may be activated by and avoid situations and stimuli that do not actually pose a threat.

People with PTSD have a hyperactive amygdala. They show a decrease in functional ability in the ventromedial prefrontal cortex, the part of the cortex that regulates emotional responses triggered by the amygdala. When the amygdala senses a threat, it "lights up," and the neural pathway to the ventromedial prefrontal cortex turns off. PTSD symptoms, including fear, anxiety, startle responses, intrusive recollections, and even flashbacks, become more intense. The brain responds not only to the trauma experience, but also other people showing fear. The person develops problems keeping emotions under control, inhibiting their reactions to perceived threats, correctly reading other people, and making good decisions.

People with a highly overactive amygdala have problems trusting others, are less able to access their own emotional intelligence, and cannot calm themselves easily. When triggered, their memory becomes compromised, and their empathy vanishes; they forget that other people's angry or rude behavior is a function of that person's emotional state not their own. As a result, they can be easily slighted and have difficulty understanding that other people's reactions are not personally directed.

An officer came to me for treatment after having been involved in two officer-involved shootings. The high school across the street was beginning a track meet. As the athletes began the race, the coach shot the starting gun. The officer suddenly dove onto my office floor and took cover behind a wing chair. After a moment he blinked and realized where he was. He gave me a baffled look and said, "Am I nuts, doc?" I explained that at the sound of the gunshot, his amygdala was activated, his hippocampus was unable to discriminate a starting gun from a real one, and his ventromedial prefrontal cortex was unable to overrule his fight or flight reaction. "No," I said, "Your brain is doing its job, just a little too well."

Think about the last time you were really mad at someone close to you. You probably had difficulty remembering any good things about them that would help you de-escalate. This is the reason it's a bad idea to try to resolve relationship issues when you are highly emotional. You'll likely end up doing and saying things that you will regret when you eventually calm down.

Also of interest are Broca's Area and Brodmann's Area. Broca's Area is one of the speech areas of the brain and is located in the left hemisphere of the frontal lobes. Without a functioning Broca's Area, a person cannot put thoughts and feelings into words. In her book *Too Scared to Cry: Psychic Trauma in Childhood,* Lenore Terr (1992) describes the trauma experienced by twenty-six school children who were kidnapped from their school bus in 1976. She found that the children could repeat the story of the kidnapping in a rote manner, but when pressed with the details and asked about their personal experience, they re-experienced intense emotional reactions, including rage, terror, and helplessness as they had during the kidnapping. They had enormous difficulty relating a coherent, articulate account. In the throes of a traumatic experience and afterward, people have difficulty accessing language, and may resort to swearing or calling for their mother. When this happens, the Broca's area has likely shut down.

Bessel van der Kolk (2014) found that trauma victims, who have reduced activity in Broca's Area, have increased activity in Brodmann's area, a part of the visual cortex. Thus, their words may fail them, but the horrible images remain and revisit the person in nightmares and surreal, terrifying flashbacks, like the one Mark, whom we met at the beginning of this chapter, experienced during his flashback of the Chinese market shooting. These images can remain for years after the trauma is over, unlike nontraumatic images, which are rapidly diffused to other areas of the brain.

Similarly, other sensory aspects of traumatic memories do not fade as do everyday memories. Traumatic memories stay with you in their original form, and unless they can be processed into a coherent story, lead to the same defensive reactions as if they were still happening.

DOES PTSD CHANGE YOUR BODY?

Again, the answer is yes. An ever-increasing body of literature suggests that the effects of traumatic stress are a major challenge that places a person's psychological and physical health equally at risk.

If you think about it, PTSD involves a body-wide reaction involving the endocrine system, organs, the musculoskeletal system, and anything that prepares you for "fight-or-flight." For example, cortisol, which is released in response to immediate stress to increase blood sugar and suppress the immune system, seems to be connected to some of the long-term changes that the body undergoes in times of overwhelming stress.

Chronic exposure to cortisol results in "wear and tear" on the body. Increased cortisol levels associated with PTSD may result in chronic muscle pain, hypertension, obesity, and cardiovascular disease. Sleep is also affected—you're not going to want to fall asleep if your body thinks there's a hungry tiger nearby. In addition to the above, sleep disorders are also considered risk factors for heart disease. So, it's no wonder how people with PTSD are susceptible to heart attacks and stroke.

Another physical manifestation of PTSD: panic attacks. For no apparent reason, you suddenly experience a feeling of intense fear, which can be accompanied by shortness of breath, dizziness, sweating, nausea, and a racing heart. You may think you're having a heart attack, but the ER doc says that you're "only having anxiety."

Other physical symptoms of PTSD include chronic pain, headaches, stomach pain, diarrhea, muscle cramps, and tightness in the chest, diabetes, autoimmune diseases, liver disease, irritable bowel syndrome, and fibromyalgia have also been associated with PTSD.

And just because the crisis is over doesn't mean you're home free. Many individuals who seemed to cope well at the time of the traumatic exposure experience symptoms months or years after the traumatic event.

DOES PTSD CHANGE YOUR LIFE?

A definite yes.

PTSD and related psychological problems can result in functional impairment, disruption in work and home life, and maladaptive coping strategies, including substance abuse, social isolation, breakdown of social support systems, damaged confidence and self-esteem, and suicidal thoughts or intentions. A first responder's reaction to trauma could negatively impact relationships with their families, co-workers, and potentially the public at large—in other words, the very people they are sworn to serve and protect.

Nearly one million Americans serve in law enforcement, over a million serve as firefighters, 100,000 as EMS personnel, another 100,000 work as police and public safety dispatchers, and there are numerous other first responder professionals. The issue of PTSD is significant.

WHAT ARE TRIGGERS?

After a trauma, people may experience a wide range of reactions. A sudden physical, emotional, or behavioral reaction may occur out of the blue in response to persons, places, or things associated with the trauma. This occurs when the brain doesn't process the trauma right away. The brain doesn't "know" that the memory is in the past. As a result, a person can have an intense emotional reaction—fear, anger, feeling out of control—even when there is no actual threat.

The stimuli associated with the trauma, usually in the form of sights, sounds, or smells, are called triggers. A person's reactions to triggers are called "being triggered." At times, triggers can seem to appear out of nowhere and seem to be totally unrelated to whatever situation the person is in at the moment. This can be confusing and frightening. Identification of personal triggers is an important step in the recovery process.

You know when you've been triggered. Suddenly, you feel your heart rate increase, palms become sweaty, breathing becomes shallow, and jaw tightens. The amygdala has sounded an alarm and stress hormones adrenaline and cortisol flood your system. You've entered fight or flight. When the amygdala kicks in, the connections to the prefrontal cortex turn off. Complex decision-making disappears, memory can become less trustworthy, and you feel trapped and disoriented as your amygdala screams, "DANGER. DANGER."

Triggers can be clearly related to an event or stimulus or at times seem unrelated, foreign, or disconnected. Remember that the hippocampus generalizes from small cues such as a tone in the voice, a facial expression, a certain posture or a position, odors, or sounds so even remotely related stimuli can trigger a memory. During Mark's flashback of the gruesome Chinese restaurant murders, he had been triggered by the mere smell of Chinese food. A primitive protective reaction from the deepest parts of his brain took over and he had no control over his body or conscious mind. He was immediately thrown into the scene of the murders. Literally, all reality seemed to vanish. His amygdala had hijacked his brain. It was doing its job—protecting Mark—but unfortunately with frightening results.

Most of the time a response to a trigger is not as extreme as Mark's amygdala hijacking, but no one looks forward to a sudden and unexpected physical reaction to a trauma. You only have to have one to know you never want another. Sometimes anxiety about experiencing a trigger serves to push the person into it.

There are several techniques to deal with triggers that are discussed in Chapter 11.

POSTTRAUMATIC GROWTH AND THE HERO'S JOURNEY

WHAT IS POSTTRAUMATIC GROWTH?

People who suffer significant trauma and adversity may find that their ability to cope with life is overwhelmed. They feel a sense of separation from loved ones and the world in general. They lose their purpose and the connections that previously sustained them. Those who have the courage to move through Posttraumatic Growth find that they not only discover unexpected benefits from their experience they reach a new level of functioning. They find deeper meaning and purpose in life; they feel reborn. They are more than resilient; they benefit from the trauma and thrive. Psychic wounds heal leaving a hard-won scar, a badge of heroism, representing a tougher, stronger, more aware sense of self.

According to Calhoun and Tedeschi (2103), individuals experience posttraumatic growth in many ways, yet with some common general elements. These include personal strength, relating to others, becoming aware of new possibilities in life, appreciation of life, and spirituality. These five factors may be placed in three conceptual categories: a changed sense of oneself, a changed sense of relationships with others, and a changed philosophy of life.

THE JOURNEY TO POSTTRAUMATIC GROWTH

In my work treating first responders suffering from PTSD, I noticed a remarkable pattern. On their path through recovery to posttraumatic growth, they embarked on a psychic journey, different in each person, but similar in patterns and themes. Their real-life stories were reminiscent of the work of Joseph Campbell (1973, 1991), who articulated how the classic mythic form of the stories describes the real, basic, practical patterns and principles by which individuals live and grow. The hero's journey to recovery is also inspired by the literary Hero's Journey as described by Vogler (1998) who adapted Campbell's concepts to the world of fiction screenwriting.

The stages are outlined as follows and described in more detail in Appendix A:

- Traveling from the ordinary civilian world to the world of first responders
- Developing purpose and learning to adjust to and adapt to the "extraordinary" first responder world
- Exposure to traumas, critical incidents, cumulative stress that leads to isolation, dysfunction, and psychological distress
- Loss of sense of purpose, vulnerability, the inability to continue as usual
- Refusal of the call to recovery followed by acceptance when there are no other options
- Challenging the dysfunctional first responder worldview
- Finding friends, companions, allies, mentors for support along the journey

- Defending against obstacles and self-sabotage
- Confronting addictions, isolation, anger, depression, anxiety
- The figurative death of the false self and discovery of the true self
- Looking backward: vulnerabilities that triggered the reaction to the critical incident
- Seizing the sword of self-knowledge: coping with triggers
- Returning to the community
- Return with the elixir: giving back to other first responders

The novice first responder aspires to find a purpose by saving lives, helping others, and contributing to the community. The novice leaves the ordinary civilian world behind to join the special world of first responders. To fit into the "extraordinary world" of "everyday heroes," the novice must accept the rules of the culture. These values include bravery at all costs, perfectionism, stoicism, personal sacrifice, and suppressing emotion to cope with horrible critical incidents. Finally, they learn the "game face" to appear to be in control and unaffected by adversity.

Next, overwhelming critical incidents may force the first responder to confront the inner, unmastered, psychological world. To embark on the journey through trauma to growth, a first responder must admit that there is a problem that is crippling them psychologically and needs to change. What follows is the challenge of leaving the "ordinary," frequently dysfunctional, world of the first responder and accepting the call to adventure in the form of (reluctantly) admitting vulnerability and the need to change.

Our hero almost always finds that companions, allies, friends, and mentors are essential to overcoming trauma. Without admitting vulnerability to others, they remain isolated and trapped in their own heads.

As the journey progresses, our hero first defends against, and subsequently identifies, painful patterns of self-sabotage and maladaptive coping mechanisms, such as denial, resistance anxiety, depression, chemical dependency, sexual and other addictions, isolation, and rationalization of habits that destroy relationships and careers.

With the help of mentors and peers, the first responder examines core dysfunctional beliefs that are emotionally paralyzing and support the continuation of PTSD symptoms. Mentors and companions guide the way as the hero faces internal threshold guardians in the form of ineffective coping mechanisms such as chemical dependency, denial, and resistance.

Core beliefs are challenged as the first responder approaches the Inmost Cave, the frightening place of their own psyche. The internal struggle of the Ordeal, the most critical phase in which the Hero faces the shadow of cynicism is replaced by acceptance of vulnerability as a positive human quality and a precursor of compassion. This is a frightening, and critical place they must challenge to move on. The acceptance of imperfection, vulnerability to stress, and trauma lead to adjusting to being a mortal human, an idea that is anathema to most first responders. At this stage, we see the figurative death of the false, overly defended, cynical, self-important self, and the discovery of the truly heroic, human self. Our hero overcomes their greatest fear, accepts vulnerability as a positive human quality and a precursor of compassion.

After "seizing the sword of self-knowledge," they look back to the childhood events that propelled them into the journey in the first place. The old ways die in the process of resurrection, and new coping mechanisms are learned. The hero returns, purified, to the newly defined Ordinary World, bringing the Elixir in the form of a promise to continue the journey and bring the newly found gift to others.

Self-knowledge and insight are now possible. The first responder looks backward to childhood events, early traumas, and dysfunctional patterns of behavior that triggered their reaction to the traumatic event in the first place. Our hero learns to identify triggers and begins to have insight into how to cope with them.

The warrior returns, purified, bringing an elixir in the form of a promise to continue the journey and bring the newly found gift to others.

Ultimately, the journey transforms the hero and results in redefining their purpose at a deeper, more meaningful level. They develop a dynamic awareness of themselves via the hero's journey into the unconscious. They have the potential for wisdom and greater compassion, and posttraumatic growth. Although memories and emotional distress may never completely disappear, the "emotional punch" is mitigated, and the heroes have a new way of perceiving their purpose in the world.

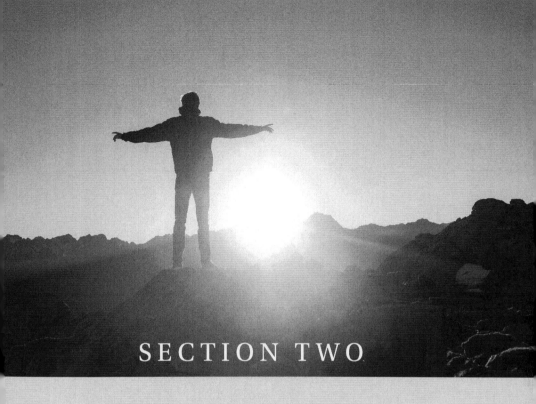

SECTION TWO

THE STORIES

Note: The stories herein are personal and raw. The names have been changed to protect individual identities.

CHAPTER 1

LEO

Line of Duty Death

*"Brotherhood is the very price and condition
of man's survival."*
CARLOS ROMULO

*"All the art of living lies in a fine mingling of letting
go and holding on."*
HENRY ELLIS

Leo is lean, wiry, and a paradox both physically and mentally. In a laid-back environment, energy emanates from his body. When engrossed in conversation, he leans forward to make a point yet strains to make eye contact. When he does look at you directly, his eyes are piercing and blue. And a bit startling—reminiscent of Steve McQueen. He has strong opinions about a lot of things but is happy to allow others to express their own ideas. His game face is confident, but occasionally without warning says something that reveals anxious self-doubt. In everyday life, he's intense. In a crisis, he's calm and focused, at least he was before the ungodly terror that was the Carr Fire.

He works in a town set in the urban-wildland interface. In 30 years of experience fighting both house fires and wildland fires, nothing could have prepared for a huge fire tornado that tore through neighborhoods wiping away all it touched including the life of his close friend. As Leo desperately tried to evacuate civilians, there seemed no way out. "I felt the presence of pure evil, like I was doomed. This was personal and the fire tornado wanted to kill me." The experience shattered his faith and the core values he believed in. He said, "It nearly stole my soul."

Leo, after suffering posttraumatic stress injuries, experienced a phenomenon few first responders suffer discuss. In overwhelming circumstances, they lose faith not only in their own abilities but in the order of the universe, even God. They are left numb to the normal human experiences of joy, love, and happiness and instead remain emotionally diminished. This chapter discusses how this spiritual crisis manifests how it can be healed, and result in posttraumatic growth and a deeper, rich spiritual life.

26 July 2018. The day the Carr Fire raced across Whiskeytown Lake, exploded into a fire tornado at Keswick Dam, and blew into Redding, California. The temperature was 113 degrees at 6 p.m. Leo was in the middle of dinner, listening to the fire's progress on a scanner, when his Battalion Chief called. The BC told Leo and his friends to respond to Land Park, a subdivision of 60 homes, some belonging to local firefighters and law enforcement officers. Leo's friends.

Leo and his crew parked their engine in a cul-de-sac and walked down an access road in the neighborhood to look at the situation. A number of civilians, homeowners, were milling around the cliffs above the Sacramento River watching the fire. The fire was still far away across the river—over a mile and a half—and no one was in a hurry.

Without warning, they were hit by an invisible, brutal wind. Leo described it as "probably 150 degrees. There was something almost supernatural about it." He looked up at me with those blue penetrating eyes. "I heard the word 'doom' in my head, over and over. It was like the wind was evil and wanted to kill me. I've never in my life experienced that before."

Leo and his crew ran back to the engine to put their gear on. Within three minutes, the fire was in the subdivision and houses were burning. By this time, the civilians were reacting. Leo screamed, "Leave. NOW!" He states, "Everyone left immediately. It's the first time I've ever had an entire crowd leave with no argument."

FIRE IN THE SKY: THE FIRE TORNADO

Hot air rose from the Carr Fire creating its own weather system, sucking oxygen, and fueling its own flames. Around 7:20 p.m., two rotating vertical plumes exploded through an inversion layer and within 30 minutes reached the height of jetliners: 42,000 feet. The plumes rotated, reaching a speed of over 143 mph, equivalent to an EF3 tornado, the strongest tornado of any type recorded in California. It scoured the ground and lofted large steel power line support towers and a steel shipping container. It grew to 1,000 feet wide, the width of three football fields, and reached a temperature of 2,700 degrees, hot enough to melt an engine block. All vegetation less than one inch and dead biomass were completely consumed. The fire tornado defies description by the National Weather Service. (Cappucci, 2018)

Firefighters were the last defense, but City of Redding Fire Chief Cullen Kreider soon realized there were no more resources available to call on: "The fire is out of control. It's snowing ash in west Redding. The wind is blowing and it's still broiling hot. Man. We're in trouble." CalFire Regional Assistant Chief Michael Hebrard: "You look into the eyes of your guys, and you see this isn't normal. They'd fought other historic blazes, but never anything like this. It's never burned anything like this. Gridlock could kill everyone." CalFire Captain Shawn Raley evacuated a family from a subdivision. Suddenly debris slammed into his vehicle, shaking it violently. The truck windows blew out and the wind pushed the truck off the road. Embers blew inside onto his passengers. "I've had some close calls," he says, "but I never before felt like it was the end." (Bashoor, 2018)

The fire tornado spread in every direction faster than evacuation orders could reach civilians. The first warning for many residents occurred when fire-laden winds blew into their yards. The orange fire-sky was punctuated with thick black columns rising from burning houses. It was as loud as an oncoming train. Civilians tried to drive out, but the fire moved so fast that many abandoned their cars and ran on foot to escape. "We were within seconds of death," one said.

The fire tornado was on the ground for 80 minutes. During that time, it contorted and crushed huge transmission towers as easily as pipe cleaners, uprooted oak trees and tore off their bark, and wrapped steel poles around trees like twist ties. Everything had been sanded smooth; the earth was scoured and denuded of vegetation leaving hard-baked clay. (Wooley et al, 2019)

Leo's breathing becomes labored as he remembers being in the midst of the fire tornado: "The wind was amazingly strong and shifted continuously, coming from every direction. It blew me to the ground several times. The smoke from burning structures and vegetation was extremely thick and continuous. My eyes felt like they had chemical burns and were hard to keep open. Breathing was challenging. Visibility at times was down to about ten feet, making it difficult to drive and impossible to keep visual track of my coworkers. It seemed like exploding fireworks were being hurled at us. I tried status checks on my portable radio, but there was so much radio traffic from other resources that it was rare that I contacted my crew even though they were only one hundred feet away. The houses in the subdivision were burning to the ground. We would save one, then go back to that location and it would have burned.

"The engine was our refuge for much of the firefight. I stayed close to put out flames that threatened it while other people tried to save houses. I was afraid that the engine might stall from the lack of oxygen, and I might not be able to start it again. I knew if we lost the engine, we would die.

"Suddenly deer, coyotes, skunks, raccoons, a bobcat ran into the subdivision for shelter. I thought, 'If wild animals are coming into a burning subdivision for shelter, how bad is it outside, and is this where I'm going to die?' In my head, I heard the word 'doom' over and over.

"Police officers were running from house to house checking for residents. I thought they were going to die and wanted to tell them to get in the engine but couldn't as they were too far away, and the fire and winds were too loud. Whenever we tried to keep a structure from burning, the wind would shift, blowing fire at us causing us to retreat. It seemed like almost everything we tried did no good. I felt hopeless, frustrated, and guilty. I wanted to call my wife and tell her goodbye, but I couldn't."

At 7:38 p.m., Leo heard a call over the radio. "It was terrible. Someone radioed a mayday. He was in the middle of a road being burned over and needed a water drop. There was 'mortal fear in his voice.' Then the radio went silent, and the caller didn't respond to calls asking for his location."

At the time, Leo didn't recognize the voice of his friend, Jeremy. Jeremy had returned early from his days off to support other firefighters battling the Carr Fire. Minutes later, after he arrived at Land Park, a fire prevention captain observed the fire tornado near his location.

At midnight, Redding Fire Chief Kreider declared Stoke missing and a search was initiated. He had been caught in the fire tornado. It sucked him from his truck and flung him so far that his body wasn't found until 3:00 a.m. His truck was recognized only by a remaining tire rim.

Leo becomes tearful as he recalls finding Jeremy's body: "A battalion chief told me, 'You don't want to see this.' He kept blocking me. They wanted me to leave before they turned his body over because the hideous image of his face would be too vivid to ever forget. I said, 'How the fuck do you know what I want?'

"I began to go, but I was driven to go back and see Jeremy's face. We rolled him over to see a massive open skull fracture that occurred when the fire tornado hurled his truck against the trees. The only burns were to his hands and torso where his Nomex had been pulled off when he'd been ejected from the truck. Strangely, I was relieved because I knew he had been killed suddenly when his head hit the trees and didn't have to endure the horror and pain of being burned alive. I threw my helmet and cursed. I got on my knees and wrapped my arms around him and cried. I said I was sorry. I cried some more and said goodbye."

The crew made a ceremony of placing Jeremy in the body bag and carrying him out of the blackened landscape. Fire engines lined up along the road. Firefighters gave a solemn salute. They began a slow procession to the coroner's office. Jeremy's final stop.

In the days and weeks after, Leo felt compelled to revisit the scene of Jeremy's death. He planned to make a presentation on the Carr Fire. Then the panic attacks started: the racing heart, shortness of breath, fears of passing out or dying. He worried about his heart. He had a "blackout" and was unable to recall driving home.

And his symptoms became worse. He felt guilty for not saving Jeremy. Two years before the Carr Fire, he had turned down a prevention position in his department. Jeremy accepted it. He told himself, "It should have been me in Jeremy's truck. I'm the one who should have died."

Leo was engaged in "magical thinking," a thinking error common in first responders who perceive that "if only" they had made a different response, a tragic outcome could have been averted. It's a form of "would 'a, could 'a, should 'a," and can be quite detrimental to a first responder's psyche. (Kirchman et al, 2014)

In Leo's case, his magical thought was if he had taken the prevention job, Jeremy would not have died. On the face of it, the idea seems ridiculous. Leo had no way of predicting the future, but it was a way of feeling less out of control of an emotionally wrenching incident. The thought that follows was, "If I never make a mistake again, nothing bad will ever happen again." This, of course, is impossible in first responder careers. Bad things do happen all the time and likely will again.

The negative impact of magical thinking can devastate a first responder's self-confidence as well as their sustaining belief that they make a positive difference. If the first responder can't reconcile that a bad outcome means they are incompetent, it can even foreshorten a career.

Leo could not get the sound of Jeremy's mayday call out of his head. He went to the station to listen to it over and over torturing himself with the thought he hadn't recognized Jeremy's voice at the time Jeremy was facing imminent death. He was flooded with fears of causing someone to be hurt or killed. He never felt safe.

In addition, triggers were still paralyzing him at times. He became painfully anxious at the sound of strong winds rushing through the mountains where he lived. It nearly put him over the edge every time he felt his "fight or flight" kick in as it had during the Carr Fire. He hyperventilated after seeing something that reminded him of the fire. He spent all his time thinking of the fire or desperately trying not to think of the fire. He cried for no reason at random times, and whenever he passed a fire station. He couldn't watch videos of fires, much less witness the response to a real one.

He had a nightmare about Jeremy's truck being thrown into a tree. Upon awakening, he said, "Fuck you! You have no more power over me." In a later nightmare, a giant fiery Phoenix was laughing at him, telling him he didn't have any power over fire.

One day, he noticed a fire near the college where he was taking classes. He had a tremendous urge to respond. He feared that people would fail to evacuate. When they did, he was both relieved and guilty that he hadn't been able to assist. At the same time, when he wore his uniform in public, he found appreciation from the public uncomfortable and tried to avoid it. He didn't want praise for a job that he felt he'd failed.

One weekend, he decided to go camping with a friend. He had an eerie and terrifying experience in the wilderness while waiting for his friend to arrive. He started a campfire, settled into his chair, and placed his pistol on the chair next to him. He recalled, "The fire circle abruptly shrank, and the temperature seemed 20 degrees colder. In my head, I heard a voice say, 'If you just shoot yourself, it will all go away.' It took me back to the Carr Fire."

The voice repeated the same thing three times before he became consciously aware that he was holding his gun in his hand. He placed the gun back on the chair, but the experience shook him to the core, and he didn't tell anyone about it for days.

He stopped interacting with his wife and family. He had angry outbursts. He stopped doing things with friends. He wanted to be alone. He doubted himself and his usefulness to the world.

In The Body Keeps the Score: Brain, Mind, and Body in the Healing of Trauma (2014), Bessel van der Kolk says, "Traumatized people chronically feel unsafe inside their bodies: They keep the past alive in the form of gnawing interior discomfort. Their bodies are constantly bombarded by visceral warning signs, and, to control these processes, they often become experts at ignoring their gut feelings and in numbing awareness of what is played out inside. They learn to hide from themselves.

"The more people try to push away and ignore internal warning signs, the more likely they are to take over and leave them bewildered, confused, and ashamed. People who cannot comfortably notice what is going on inside become vulnerable to respond to any sensory shift either by shutting down or by going into a panic—they develop a fear of fear itself."

In other words, the way you know you have a posttraumatic stress injury is that it's always there with you. Leo most definitely had a posttraumatic stress injury.

Fortunately for Leo, the allied agencies offered therapy sessions after the Carr Fire-tornado incident. He had a session of Brainspotting, a treatment developed by David Grand that reprocesses negative emotions, that helped him envision that Jeremy came back and told Leo not to blame himself. He later had EMDR, a technique developed by Francine Shapiro in the 1980s to treat negative memories, to help him release some of the agony he felt about the mayday call.

He still needed intensive treatment and attended the West Coast Posttrauma Retreat (WCPR), a 6-day program for first responders whose lives have been impacted by work trauma. He worked hard in the classes and therapy sessions. Slowly, his symptoms began to abate. He became less anxious, although he was triggered occasionally. He slowly began to socialize and engage in activities, like kayaking, that he loved. He worked with his wife on improving communication.

He hoped to finish out his career, but fate wasn't in agreement and his heart wasn't cooperating with the plan. During one call, he experienced arrhythmia and was taken to the hospital. A cardiologist diagnosed him as having a third-degree heart block and installed a pacemaker. He began to wonder if he was physically capable of fighting fires. Or emotionally capable. Then there were those 24-hour shifts, and Leo was not a young man anymore.

> Leo had accepted the call to his inner adventure. He met mentors who inspired him to cross the threshold to a special, inner world in which he looked at himself like never before. He had tests, such as filing a workers' compensation claim based on a psychological injury and heart problems, yet he also had mentors and allies who helped him negotiate his way through the vagaries of the bureaucracy. He had traveled far, but he was not yet finished with his hero's journey. There was another step in his self-knowledge and growth—the road back.

Leo was the oldest child of three in his family. Several months after the Carr Fire, Leo's father became ill. Leo traveled several hours to visit him out of state while he was in the hospital. It was not an easy trip. On the drive home, Leo experienced "blackouts" for a part of the trip. When he arrived home, he could not recall much of it. "I was stone-cold sober," he insisted. "This has happened to me before when I was under extreme stress."

When his father died soon after, Leo felt an emotional onslaught of unresolved trauma from his childhood.

He described his father as a bigoted, cruel alcoholic who abused Leo and his mother. Leo dreaded his father coming home at night—the abuse usually began at the dinner table.

His father wasn't content to limit his cruelties to Leo's mother. He devised a game with Leo. He would demand Leo to look at him, then pull back his fist and stop just short of punching his face. If Leo flinched, his father would demean him. Leo learned to avoid his father's stare, and subsequently eye contact with everyone.

Leo spent much of his adolescence trying to stay away from his father.

Leo said, "My father never gave me a voice. My home was never safe. I wasn't allowed to talk, and if I did, my father would knock me across the room. He'd constantly tell me I was an idiot. I learned to never speak up or look people in the eye. It has affected my marriage and being a father. I'm working hard on relearning that pattern."

Other tragedies marked Leo's family. His brother committed suicide. His parents divorced and his mother remarried a sex offender. He and his sister had conflicts over their father's estate. Despite his father's abusive behaviors and the troubles in his family, Leo persevered. He finished school and started a successful career with the fire service.

Many first responders of all types grow up in dysfunctional, even violent, homes. Perhaps this drives them to enter a career in which they become helpers, protectors, and defenders of the helpless and injured. At some level, conscious or unconscious, they want to make sure they prevent others from being hurt in the ways they were. Even with that noble goal, they often are not free of their past. When a critical incident occurs that triggers unresolved memories of the past, the emotions that come up can seem raw, bring up old vulnerabilities, and make coping with that trauma much more difficult.

Is there a connection between Leo's childhood and his reaction to Jeremy's death and the Carr Fire? The fire and Jeremy's death triggered profound feelings of vulnerability, not being good enough, helplessness, and powerlessness. Those states are similar to the childhood reactions that had been buried for years as he worked hard to rise in his career, only to surface again after Jeremy's death and give him an emotional punch.

Previously, Leo took part in an EMDR session during which he processed childhood memories. Leo did much to prepare for it, including developing a "resource installation" to give him a backup to use when experiencing difficult emotions.

While using bilateral stimulation, he created a "place" where he could go in his head. His place was a beautiful meadow. He focused on the sights, sounds, and smells that could be found in a meadow and felt serene. He then described his strengths—the parts of his personality that helped him survive all the arduous trials in his life. He realized that no matter how bad things got for him, he was able to put aside the pain, focus on the good, and appreciate nature. Then he was asked to pick an advisor, someone who had his back and could encourage him. He chose a supervisor who would tell him to get in touch with his spiritual side and call him on things he needed to correct.

During the EMDR, Leo was able to express his rage at his father for all the abuses he had inflicted on his family. He came to understand he had internalized his father's judgmental and critical attitude toward him, thus setting himself up to believe that he had failed Jeremy and contributed to his death. He saw that his thinking was magical, and not based on reality.

He also delved into his father's own tragic childhood. By understanding his father as a wounded child, he was able to conceive of forgiving him. In a sense, he entered an abyss that had terrified him since childhood and fought the beast of anger that he had tried to suppress for so long. The emotional punch began to soften.

"Then something amazing happened," he said. "I remembered some good times with my dad. We used to watch Bugs Bunny cartoons on Saturday mornings. And my father taught me the love of the outdoors.

"I realize that he was just a human. A tormented one, a messed up one, but a human."

Has Leo experienced posttraumatic growth? I think so.

He has sought new possibilities in his life. He became a valued peer at WCPR and helps other first responders in a way he never imagined he could before. Although he can be by the stories of clients, he is becoming adept at working through his emotional reactions.

He teaches at a local college, a long-term goal he never had time for before he retired. His relationships with his family have improved. He communicates with his wife and kids with more vulnerability.

He has forgiven his father, freeing him from the hate he felt for so long. Through the loss of Jeremy, he learned how to mourn, but also appreciate life at a new level and find gratitude for the wonders of the world.

And he is exploring his spirituality through Native American teachings. He related a story to me about watching a bald eagle fly and the hope he viscerally felt for the future.

Many months after the Carr Fire, Leo asked me to go to Jeremy's site with him. We drove across the dam where the fire tornado started and up the hill to the neighborhood it demolished. It's still barren of vegetation, but homes are being rebuilt and patches of green appear sporadically. We looked over the cliff to the river where the wild animals and some humans had fled to save themselves from the fire.

We turned onto a two-lane road. No other vehicles were around, and we had the place to ourselves. After a mile or so, we came to Jeremy's memorial. It seemed small in the distance and grew as we got closer. Next to a large picture of Jeremy grinning ear to ear, lay bouquets of fresh flowers, half a dozen American flags, an assortment of caps and helmets from different fire departments, a bottle of whiskey or two, and a Shasta Strong poster thanking the first responders for saving lives and homes.

We stayed for a moment in silent thoughts. Leo asked if I wanted to move on. I nodded and we negotiated over earth permanently scorched and barren from the fire. Leo stopped behind some bushes.

"This is where he died and where we found him. And where I turned him over and saw that he had a head injury." He looked around and pointed to a truck tire. "That's what's left of his truck. And that's the tree he hit."

"How are you doing with coming here again?" I asked him, looking for any signs of stress.

"It's better every time. I feel more at peace." He smiled and looked me in the eye. "There was evil was here, but Jeremy's spirit has conquered it."

CHAPTER 2

DILLON, PART 1
Suicide of a Colleague

"Of this alone even God is deprived, the power of making things that are past never to have been."
AGATHON, POET

Dillon sat in his patrol vehicle outside the Alcoholics Anonymous meeting trying to work up the courage to walk in. The image of Lee's body kept exploding inside his head. No matter how much he drank, the bloody remains of the bastard's head stayed right in his line of sight. He needed another drink, but more than that he needed to talk. It was 7 a.m. and he was dressed in his highway patrol uniform.

He'd already been to the highway patrol office at 5 a.m. that morning, but he couldn't force his legs out of the car to go in for morning briefing. He'd convinced himself that he was ready to go back to patrol after taking some time off to recover from his latest critical incident. That wasn't working, so he drove to AA with the thought he'd go to a meeting before work. Instead, he reached into the glove compartment and picked up the booze bottle he'd hidden there. He took the first swig straight from the bottle.

The next thing he knew, he woke up at home on the couch. He couldn't recall how he got there. His wife walked in, none too happy. She handed him the phone. His sergeant wanted to know where the hell he was and the reason he hadn't shown up for work. The following day, he went into the office and turned in his gun and badge. He asked himself how he'd managed to become such a colossal fuck up.

Dillon grew up in a small town. He played baseball and the piano and enjoyed learning from his mechanic father how to work on cars. He loved driving and tended to push the speed limit at times. His mother was a stay-at-home parent, providing the emotional support for the family.

His high school shop teacher, a former highway patrolman, would bring Zenith, a law enforcement magazine, to class. Dillon poured over every issue and quickly realized his career choice was law enforcement, specifically, the highway patrol. He looked more like a cop than anyone had a right to, growing into an outstanding six-foot-two beefcake with deep blue eyes accented by a chiseled face and an easy smile that brightened the room. In another life, he might find work as a romance novel cover boy.

During his senior year in high school, Dillon's best friend enlisted in the Army. Dillon wanted to make a difference, in society, by helping to maintain control and order in his environment. Because he was too young to apply for a peace officer position, he headed down to talk to the Army recruiter without even telling his parents. With his spotless background and intelligence, he was given a high-security clearance and assigned to the Military Police.

Dillon spent most of his tour of duty in the Middle East dodging SCUD missiles. He doesn't stress about any specific critical incidents— just the day-to-day horrors of war. When he was honorably discharged, he moved back to his hometown, where he enrolled in Administration of Justice courses at the local college. He worked at a fast-food joint and applied to law enforcement agencies. He and his high school girlfriend reconnected. She became pregnant, and Dillon was ready to do the right thing. They married around the time he entered the academy for the finest law enforcement agency in the state.

Dillon thrived in the highway patrol academy. His familiarity with cars and outstanding driving skills gave him the necessary confidence to excel in emergency vehicle operations. He was near the top academically. The Academy taught him to think of himself as a guardian of society. Yes, he'd heard a lecture or two about job stress encountered in law enforcement but hadn't paid attention. He knew that he'd be confronted with dangers and critical incidents inconceivable to the general citizen, but he was equipped to take charge because he was strong, tough, and had the highest standards of training. He had the confidence to handle anything.

Graduation day was the best day of his life. During the ceremony, he was honored with the most valuable award. His wife and parents attended the ceremony and looked at him like he was a hero. He imagined that life couldn't be much better. He'd reached his life's goal, the only career he'd ever wanted.

Dillon had left the ordinary civilian world once he enlisted in the Army and became a warrior. When he was discharged, he no longer saw life in the same way, and didn't fit psychologically into a safe and sheltered society. The only path he could see was to continue his life as a protector and become a peace officer. His new world taught him that if he was well trained and confident, he could cope with any crisis. First responders who know better call this "drinking the Kool-Aid," a phrase deriving from the nightmare of the Jonestown bloodbath in Guyana in 1978. The phrase has come to mean, "blindly follow." In first responder parlance, it refers to the belief that the organization has become your family and that it will take care of you in exchange for your loyalty and putting your life on the line. When first responders sign up and put themselves in harm's way, they do not expect to feel betrayed by their agencies. Hence, "drinking the Kool-Aid." The result is that their worldview can become dysfunctional; once it is shattered, they no longer feel safe or valued.

Dillon began his career in a large, busy city and after a few years transferred to a smaller town close to his parents. He was young and cocky and expected to have an interesting and fun job. He looked forward to some action and being able to drive fast in vehicle pursuits. An incident in which a man lost his life burned in a car because the response to the call was delayed affected him deeply. He recalls, "Had the responders on call gotten there faster, it might have made a difference in that guy's life. That scene stuck with me—I carried that through my entire career. After that, when I got called, I wanted to be first on scene. And if I heard someone else get a call and I wasn't doing anything, I went to that call. Now did I ever make a difference? I don't know, you never know. But I do know that it is probably one of the reasons that I was always a shit magnet and involved in everything, because I rolled to everything."

As a young officer with few critical incidents in his emotional backpack, he didn't realize that his self-expectations and self-confidence were unreasonably inflated. An incident on a summer's day didn't do much to slow him down. While assigned to a detail to recover stolen cars, he was driving his unmarked patrol car on a two-lane highway paralleling a canal and got a call about a drunk driver. He hung a U-turn and charged off in the direction of the drunk driver.

Dillon tells the rest, "I was flying just trying to get there to intercept this guy and I come up behind a farm truck, slowing down. God, why is he going so frigging slow? Like under the speed limit type of slow. I'm on the brakes slowing down and I finally just go around him and I'm looking at him, old-timer in a white truck, as I'm going by and I'm thinking, well, no, this is not my drunk. That old man is just being cautious. And I'm back on the gas. I direct my attention to the front and as soon as look forward, this yellow flash goes by in my left peripheral vision. It would have been the driver's side window. Well, after the smoke had settled, that sign said 15 mph and showed a sharp right turn and right after, a sharp left turn. By that time, I'm probably doing every bit of 80 plus. Just then I see the road. It's probably 90 degrees to the right and there's a canal. Like, if you go straight off, you're in the canal. I turn to the right as hard as I can, and I never touch the brake. Because that's how you handle it. This was before traction control, before ABS and all that. As soon as the car starts to slide, I hit the gas because that's how you drive out of a slide. And I'm holding on across that sliding, and I'm going to the right, and I'm like I'm going to make this . . . it's all so slow in my head. I'm going to make this. I've got power steering, I'm sliding. I've got this. And it would have worked out perfectly if it was just a right turn.

"But then it went immediately back to the left. There was a point where if it just went right, I'd have straightened out and drove through it, but now I was out of road, facing the wrong way when it banked to the left and I remember looking out the driver's side window going, oh shit, I'm going to crash.

"And there's another canal on the other side of that left-hand turn. It's just canals everywhere. I fly off the road into the dirt. It seemed so slow. I put my hand on the bottom of the steering wheel, I put my knees together and I'm looking left. I put my chin down to my chest. I remember saying, 'this sucks.' Then it started to roll. Crash, crash, crash. Then it got quiet, and then I felt the impact because my head got slammed back into the seat. I heard glass shattering, and then I heard what it sounds like when you drop a big rock into a bucket—KERPLUNK. I'd gone into the canal upside down and it got so dark. I remember taking one deep breath and I sank into the canal, upside down, in the dark, in a patrol car.

"It was in a caged car, light bar on the top, all the back glass had broken out. That's how the water came in so quickly. The driver and passenger windows and front windshield were all still intact. When I was rolling, the light bar that's secured to the roof had smashed down and clipped over the top of the door, so it acted as a lock. The exterior doors would not open. The windows were powered so they wouldn't open. Now all this is happening in the dark, upside down, underwater. I'm holding my breath. I remember I took three distinct tries to get my seatbelt off, and when my seatbelt finally came off, I felt pressure on my headfirst, so I knew I was upside down. So, I righted myself and I'm hitting with my elbow on the window. Nothing. I got my baton, and I could hear it underwater. Tink, tink, tink. Nothing. I'm struggling. I move, and my head comes into where the passenger's feet would be. There was air in there, so I had from my shoulders up in this little lifesaving area that was not full of water. I remember stomping on the passenger's window—nothing.

"So, I grab my gun, I know the window is down there. I don't know why I didn't put it under water to pull the trigger, but I just thought, 'Oh,

I need to keep my gun out of the water to shoot down the window and I hope I don't shoot myself in the leg when I do this.' So, I'm holding it next to my head, my left ear, pointing it down to where I think the window is, and I pull the trigger. I felt my left foot go down, so that meant that the glass had shattered. But my God, were my ears ringing.

"It was stupid to keep the gun out of water. It should have worked underwater because the bullets are encased so tightly that the explosion takes place in the casing. It had already been underwater. So, if it wasn't going to work, it wasn't going to work. At least I would have saved the noise in my ears.

"I holstered my gun, and I went back underwater and swam out. I got some cuts and tore up my uniform and stuff going through the glass. I popped up out of the canal, and it was the funniest thing. There's that fucking white truck that I had just passed. I see it up there and then I look closer, and I see the old man's white hair and eyes. That's all I see is white hair and eyes over the hood of his truck. He sees me and he stands up slowly, and he's like, 'You all right?' I'm like, 'Yeah.' He goes, 'I was going to come help you, but then I heard a gunshot, so I didn't know what the fuck was going on and I got the hell out of there.' He comes to the bank, and he helps pull me out. Somebody had seen it, somebody called from somewhere. They were doing a status check. My radio wasn't working, and they status-checked dispatch, status-checked everybody. Apparently, when I didn't answer, there was a last known location, so there were units rolling hot from everywhere.

"They find me and put me in the ambulance, and they take me to the hospital. That's when my lifelong back issues started. They didn't really do anything—not even x-rays. The doctor was kind of a joke. He sets me up. 'Hold your arms out. Push on them, does that hurt?' I say, 'A little bit.' He says, 'Turn the other way, can you lift your leg? Okay, you'll be all right. Just take this pill.'

"I was off for a couple of days and the department drove me back out to the scene to watch the car get pulled out. They had to use a great big rig tow. The canal was only about eight feet deep, but, you know, when you're upside down, you only need a couple of feet to be in trouble.

They're pulling it out, and there's fish and crawdads and shit falling out of the windows. I got my stuff out. Three days later, I finally dumped out my briefcase and there is a crawdad in it, still alive.

"I went back to work, and they called me Aqua Man. The Chevy emblem from the car that I totaled was glued to my pigeonhole where I got my mail in the office. It was never treated as a traumatic incident. It was just kind of made fun of, and I got what is called a Form 2, which is a written disciplinary action because I destroyed a police car driving too fast for conditions. It began with a paragraph of this date, this time, you were driving too fast, violated policy, you ruined equipment, $20,000. Shame on you. Two or three paragraphs after that it said, 'However, having the presence of mind, you were in an intense situation, blah, blah, blah, you used your emergency training, you shot your gun, you saved your life, you could have died, awesome job.' So, my disciplinary thing sounded like a good job letter. But it was really a disciplinary letter, so it was kind of funny.

"But that changed my cowboy ways when it came to driving. I still love to this day cars and going fast, but I'm a little more cautious on a road that I've never been on before. I don't drive like a maniac. I take it easy. I never made a good passenger after that. Oh my god, I've stomped on the emergency brake on my side as a passenger. I yell at the driver to slow down. I'm always stressing about getting in a crash because there's no control from the passenger seat. And I still want to be the one who drives most of the time.

The instant Dillon got the call and decided to respond, his thalamus kicked into gear. Recall that the thalamus is part of the "emotional brain," or limbic system. Its job is to take sensory information from our eyes, ears, nose, and skin and process it into a coherent, integrated experience. It says, "This is what is happening to me." The thalamus then routes the information in two directions, down to the amygdala and up to the cortex, which is the center of our conscious thought.

The amygdala is our smoke detector. It quickly identifies whether or not something is relevant to our survival. The amygdala works in conjunction with a nearby structure, the hippocampus. The job of the hippocampus is to connect new input to past experience.

As Dillon began the pursuit, he experienced excitement and anticipation. His amygdala sent a message to the hypothalamus and brain stem to release stress hormones. His adrenal glands began to release adrenaline. His heart rate accelerated, his lungs began to work harder, his blood vessels dilated, his muscles tensed, his pupils dilated, and his intestines slowed down, all to prepare him for fight or flight.

Under these physical circumstances, overwhelming fear of being unable to handle the situation could be expected. On the other hand, Dillon had the training and confidence to psychologically and physiologically override, even benefit from the level of arousal, and move forward. Unlike untrained civilians, first responders benefit from this level of arousal because it promotes decisive action and survival.

The information from the thalamus then routed to Dillon's cortex, and he made a conscious decision to begin the pursuit. He focused on finding the vehicle in question, so focused in fact that he became annoyed when the white truck appeared in front of him and slowed him down. Under these conditions, his sensory perception was altered. He decided to pass the white truck and didn't consciously "see" the 15 MPH sign on the side of the road.

The instant he realized that the road turned 90 degrees and he was going too fast, the thalamus again sent instantaneous signals to the amygdala. This time, the amygdala recognized a real threat and went into alarm mode. Dillon immediately reacted to keep the vehicle on the road. Because the signals to the frontal cortex take several milliseconds longer, his training came into play before he even realized the danger he was in. He turns to the right, he doesn't touch the brake, he slides, and he hits the gas. During a critical incident, several milliseconds seem nearly forever. Finally, after he begins reacting, the information reaches his cortex, and he tells himself, "You got this."

Then the left bend appears, and he knows he won't make it. As he realized that he was "out of road," he felt anger, disbelief, fear, and perhaps a little numbing. The stress hormones are flooding his system. He crashes, he rolls, and he lands in the canal. Again, his training takes over. Before the information about his situation reaches his cortex, he reacts. By this time, information is coming in too fast, and the thalamus can't process everything at once. Normal memory processing falls apart. Sights, sounds, smells, and touch become isolated, dissociated fragments. Time freezes. The incident seems to last a long time, yet telling the story takes many seconds longer than the actual incident.

At last, the information reaches the cortex. He consciously thinks about how to exit the car; he begins trying everything. He releases his seat belt and realizes he's upside down. He turns "up" to find air. He hits the glass, kicks the glass. He can recall the "tink, tink" sound of his baton against the windshield.

He tries his gun. He shoots out the windshield. Later, after the sound of the gunshot hurts his ear, he realizes it was "stupid" to not put the gun under water right near the glass. But in the moment, he didn't have time to process that through the conscious part of his brain. Nonetheless, what saves him is his training to keep trying to survive.

What is the reason Dillon didn't develop a clear posttraumatic psychological injury from the crash? He had every sign of the physical and psychological arousal that could accompany such an injury. The answer is that his life experience and training helped him with the primary arousal he experienced. He maintained command presence. He was victorious in controlling himself in this incredibly high stress, life-threatening incident. He didn't lose his self-esteem, his self-confidence, or his belief in his ability to do what's right and survive.

In fact, the most difficult parts of the incident were being tagged with the moniker "Aqua Man," and being given a cursory medical exam that missed the development of his lifelong back injury. These factors seem to bother him more than the actual crash. The perception that he was mocked and overlooked was psychologically more troubling than nearly losing his life. As we will see, secondary arousal, which can come from self-doubt, feelings of inadequacy, and feeling like no one has your back, can be the type of arousal that can kill a career.

Self-confidence is a double-edged sword. Without it, a first responder wouldn't enter the battle, but when a call goes wrong, or the first responder begins to believe the people he relies on don't have his back, self-expectations can be shattered, self-criticism and self-blame rush in, and confidence erodes. Posttraumatic stress reactions can set in, especially when fears and doubts aren't addressed.

Dillon's confidence was finally shaken on a cold winter day when he'd been on the job for five years. He still looked forward to each workday and was eager to get to the office a little early. That day the air was crisp, and the sun was a faint orange glow just below a cloudbank resting above the horizon.

As pulled into the agency lot, he thought about the office drama of the week. A fellow patrolman, Sergeant Lee, was rumored to be having an extramarital affair with a young cadet and had been caught drinking on the job. He now was the subject of an internal affairs investigation. Dillon was too busy with his job, his young family, and life in general to pay much attention to the gossip. Besides, Lee was a nice guy who'd helped Dillon out a time or two. Dillon trusted him enough to allow their kids to play together and have occasional family barbeques in Lee's backyard.

Dillon tapped in the gate code and drove his personal vehicle into the gated lot. A few sprinkles of rain fell onto the windshield. He strode through the building and went to his locker to get some rain gear before he jogged down the stairs to the vehicle bay where his patrol vehicle was parked.

Dillon immediately sensed that something wrong. The smell was off. He switched on the overhead light and noticed Lee's vehicle parked outside the bay. The driver and passenger doors were both open, but Dillon couldn't see Sergeant Lee. He thought, "What the heck?" He called out and began to walk around the other side of the patrol car. With the next step, something squished beneath his boot. Time seemed to stop. Suddenly, the picture solidified. The sergeant's body was hanging out the door of the car, but where was his head? Dillon looked down and had an urge to vomit. Most of the sergeant's head and brain matter were scattered over the floor. A shotgun lay between the seats.

Dillon froze. Nothing in his military career or the academy had prepared him for this. After what seemed like forever, he went into operations mode, took control of the scene, called for an ambulance, and contacted the captain.

He describes his experience: "I saw a big pool of coagulated blood and brains on the ground. It hit me hard. I didn't know what to think because I just thought it was an accident at first. For a while I was sad. I didn't understand it. And then I was mad.

"That day, it started to rain. The ISU, the investigative services unit, is down there investigating it. I go downstairs and they're all standing under the cover of the garage looking out at Lee about 15 feet away from there in the rain just kind of chit-chatting. I remember losing my shit on them. 'What the fuck are you doing?' I said. 'Why is he still here? Why is he sitting there? Why don't you cover him up? Why don't you put a canopy over him?' So, they start moving around—they finally put a pop-up tent over the scene. Now I get it, it's an investigation, it's either a murder, it's a suicide, or it's an accident. I get it. It's got to be what it's got to be for a while. But I was really angry that day because they just left him out in the rain, and everyone was tracking his blood and brains all over the place.

"The funeral was open casket. They had all this make-up all over his head. It was weird. Then his wife, widow, they take . . . the State sends them to the capitol. He died in January, so in the spring, they do police officer memorial week. So, I escorted her to the capitol for a couple of days so the governor can give her the 'We're Sorry Your Husband's Dead Plaque.' And then they do a national ceremony in DC for all the police officers that were killed. I met the president on that one. I escorted her, that one was almost a week-long thing. But yeah, the incident didn't go away quickly. It was around for a while in my head."

At the time of the incident, his department didn't have mandatory debriefings or arrangements for formal critical incident stress management. "It's before I was educated on debriefing. After it had happened, I remember being at home and getting a call from one of the sergeants going 'Hey, there's a counselor down here in the office if you want to talk to him about anything. They're going to be here until three o'clock or whatever.' Okay, thanks, I said, and hung up. I wasn't about to tell anyone that I was having trouble getting Lee out of my head."

Dillon went home that night and ate dinner with his family. He didn't have much appetite and didn't mention the incident. When his wife learned from social media that Officer Lee had killed himself, Dillon didn't tell her what he'd witnessed. He downplayed the disgust, fear, and horror he'd experienced. He was a cop, which meant he wasn't vulnerable to stressors that would devastate the ordinary person. If he talked about how he felt or asked for help, he'd appear weak. Besides, he told himself, why upset his wife?

Denial of vulnerability helps first responders keep going in terrifying circumstances to finish the job. The problem with denial is when a person walls off unpleasant emotions or reactions, they at times suppress positive ones like love. Dillon was beginning to believe that no one outside his work would be able to understand or support him.

Yes, there was the Employee Assistance Number on the office wall, but he knew if anyone found out he saw a shrink he would be the butt of many a joke. Without realizing it, he was beginning to wonder if anyone inside the department had his back. He'd been told at the Academy that the department was his "family." Was it true? He decided he needed to appear completely resilient and unaffected. Anything less would be career suicide.

The stress began to wear on him. He began creating psychological distance from his family, and everyone else. He couldn't get the sight of the remains of Lee's head out of his mind. Sometimes it seemed so close he could touch it. Sometimes it was there when he closed his eyes. The guilt he felt was overwhelming—why hadn't he known Lee was in such bad shape? Why hadn't he reached out to help him? Dillon began to see himself as a piece of shit. He ruminated about his weaknesses and faults, and began sliding into isolation, mental fatigue, and depression, the hallmarks of posttraumatic stress.

Dillon's words: "Being a cop is perfect for someone who isolates because you can be at work and doing your job and isolate all day. You're in your car, you're driving around, and your mind is wherever your mind is. You get a call, you go out and do your thing, you write a ticket, and you get back in your car. You're around people and you're not around anybody you really have to talk to. It's pretty much all business. So, you know normally, when you ask a cop who's early in treatment if they are isolating, they'll say, 'Maybe once in a while.'

"My thought of isolation was off duty. Did I isolate? When you are off duty, you are either asleep or not awake for very long. You're kind of doing the show. But in hindsight, looking back, I isolated the whole time I was at work. I didn't like being around anybody. First, it was eight hours and then we went to twelve-hour shifts. Twelve hours of just me, and the world can leave me the fuck alone. I'll go out and save people's lives and then they can leave me alone. And then when you get off work, I could drink, so it made being around people a little bit easier to be around.

"The telltale sign of a law enforcement officer isolating is that cops love to have coffee. It's what they call it. It doesn't matter if you go have lunch, whatever, they just want to have coffee. You meet up with another unit, you go here you chat, you go eat and talk, you go hang out under an overpass for a little bit and talk. And when Lee happened to me, I didn't want to do any of that. I'd get a call or text from whomever I was working with. 'Hey, you want to go meet?' And I'd say, 'No, I've got to go do . . . whatever. I'm out in the boonies, I'm too far.' I would just avoid other officers too."

Dillon returned to his duties and tried to suppress the physical reactions that left him feeling like he was losing his mind. He kept having vivid nightmares, but found if he had a drink before bed, he couldn't remember the dreams. The drink became two drinks, and sometimes more. He told his wife alcohol helped him sleep.

"I would see his face and that big bushy mustache and glasses just as clear as day and then I started having this awful dream where I'd . . . it's hard for me to recall it because I've tucked it so far away, but it feels like a gunfight and the bullets were going slow and toward the end. I'm falling by a curb, and someone shoots me in the head. I can hear it, I can feel it, I can taste it."

Dillon would ruminate, that is, think about things over and over. Rumination can be a good thing for first responders if it helps them figure out how to improve their performance, but it's not helpful if their repetitive thoughts center on inadequacy and shame.

Over time, Dillon's wife started "acting bitchy." She complained about his drinking and said that even when he was home, he wasn't there mentally. He started spending more time in the garage, drinking, working on his racecars, and listening to talk shows on the radio. He didn't even feel like going to office barbeques. One day he had too much to drink. His wife flew into a rage, over what he can't recall, and threatened divorce. "Fine," he said, and packed his bag. For the next month, he slept on a friend's couch.

Dillon was having more and more difficulty going to work. Finally, he realized he could not go back into that vehicle bay every day for the rest of his career. He had to get away from the grisly visions of Lee's brains that kept popping into his mind. He put in for a transfer to another office. It was granted and he moved to his new city without his family. He rented an apartment and saw his daughter on his days off. His wife filed for divorce. He signed the papers without argument.

Dillon explains: "I thought, 'I don't need to talk to a fucking counselor. It's not going to change anything.' Yet, in hindsight, as I sit here talking today, it's huge. And for the last, I don't know, five, six, seven years, anybody that I've mentored or helped get a job at the agency, like a friend or somebody's son, what do I have to say to them? I say, 'Get a tune-up every year. You need to talk to a therapist even if it's about the dinner you had the night before. At least once a year just go in and barf up all the shit that you're holding down.'

"Nobody ever told me that. I think my life would have been a lot different had mental health been more important in the department and not such a big black thing. I finally called the whatever-it's-called, you know, the 'you're going to die number' that's practically hidden in the office kitchen. The guy who answered wanted to take my name and phone number. He said he'd route it to my commander on Monday. 'No thanks," I said. 'Fuck off.'

"But when I was desperate enough to finally call the 800 number. It was a call center on the East Coast. It was obvious to me, and because we're cops, and we can pick this stuff apart. We're not the normal person that calls and thinks the person on the other end is actually trying to help when they're just taking information. We're suspicious, we ask questions. The dude was on the opposite coast. He wasn't even a member of the highway patrol. How useless.

"You know my car crash was significant. But it didn't make me stumble around aimlessly and wonder about things. The first thing in my career that stopped me dead in my tracks and just had me questioning things was Lee. You know? And I never talked to anybody about it."

During the next year or so, Dillon responded to the "usual" gruesome accidents, baby deaths, shootings, and suicides. Sometimes he didn't drink for a week or two; sometimes he drank a fifth a night.

One summer weekend, he ran into Jan at a barbeque. He was immediately attracted to her exotic beauty. He put on his game face, wooed her with his smile and charm, and married her. They moved into a nice home, and he hid his demons from everyone. However, he couldn't hide the negativity in his mood and thoughts, the irrational self-blame over every little thing, the lack of hope in the future, and blowing up over minor incidents. Some days, he became so frustrated and impatient that he couldn't work on his cars. Finally, at his worried wife's insistence, he agreed to seek therapy. He began to spill out his demons, and even managed to stop drinking for a while.

Things went well for a while until the week in which "something was dead every day."

On his Monday, Dillon responded to an overturned truck that had crushed the occupants. On Tuesday, he responded to a trailer fire in which a child, the same age as Dillon's daughter, burned to death. Later in his shift, he responded to a head-on collision in which a mother who was driving died. Her young children, who had been in the back seat, were screaming for their mom.

On Wednesday, a man driving an ATV had a heart attack and died. Another serious head-on crash occurred later that day. Right before

Dillon's shift was over, he was called to a scene in which a mentally disturbed man attacked two other men with an axe and chopped them to pieces. The man threatened the responding officers, who finally used deadly force on him.

Something dead every day. He willed himself to not think about Lee's body. He was okay. He was on patrol—the reason he loved his job. He was holding it together, but the worst was soon to come.

On a cold Friday morning, the weather turned nasty—the sky dumped rain and hail like the gods were trying to destroy the world. Dillon responded to a vehicle that slid off the road on a stretch covered by hail. He and a local firefighter, Rich, were assisting the motorist when another car hit the same stretch of slippery road and flew off, barely missing Dillon. He hollered to Rich that they needed to get out of the area. Just then, a third vehicle flew off the road and slammed into Rich at 60 mph, killing him instantly. Dillon escaped by diving into a swale. He sustained injuries that were significant, but not life-threatening.

The hardest part of this incident for Dillon, besides the death of his friend, happened at Rich's funeral. In front of hundreds of grievers, the department chiefs brought Dillon, in his dress blues, to the front of the auditorium and hailed him a hero. He didn't feel like a hero at all. He felt like a failure. He'd abandoned Rich on the side of the road, and Rich died. He was overcome with guilt and shame. He thought of Lee. He'd failed Lee, too. His worldview was shattered. His core beliefs about his ability to take charge and help others were destroyed. He was broken.

First responders deal with the inconceivable every day and develop changes in their physiology and brain chemistry compared to people who experience a single trauma. When the amygdala, the "smoke detector" that identifies whatever is happening is important to survival, is overactive or under constant stress, it can't turn off the fight or flight mechanism. This leads to constant, overwhelming anxiety. The amygdala works in conjunction with the hippocampus, the part of the brain that connects new experience to past experience.

Under sufficient stress, the hippocampus can shrink, rendering the person unable to understand the context and unable to distinguish what's truly a threat. In addition, constant stress can harm the neurons in the prefrontal cortex, the part of the brain that helps us solve problems, control our impulses, and process and regulate our emotions. Parts of the brain that regulate pleasure and reward can become damaged, making a person more susceptible to addiction, and impairing its ability to bounce back.

The day he drove to his AA meeting and sat outside, unable to go in, the day he pulled out the bottle he'd hidden in the glove compartment and drank himself into oblivion, was almost his bottom. The day he surrendered his badge and gun to his department was his bottom. He thought he'd lost the career he loved. His wife was threatening to leave him. His self-esteem was demolished, along with his sense of purpose and relevance. Dillon had gone from the poster boy of the highway patrol to the poster child of PTSD.

We will meet Dillon again in Chapter 8.

CHAPTER 3

MAX
Serious Line of Duty Injury

*"The mystery of human existence lies not in just staying alive
but in finding something to live for."*
FYODOR DOSTOYEVKSY

Max is a tall, well-muscled blond who physically resembles the fearless Siegfried in Wagner's opera "The Ring Cycle" except he wields not a sword to slay a dragon, but a fire hose to slay wildfire. These days, his stride is long and strong not noticeably different than before the helicopter accident. His journey has been profoundly challenging, yet he has recovered every bit of the command presence he had before his critical incident.

The first time I met Max was in a group therapy session at the West Coast Posttrauma Retreat for first responders. His entire body shook with fear and anxiety. His eyes stared straight ahead in a thousand-yard stare yet trembled in a jittery nystagmus. He was barely able to communicate how he watched the blades of the chopper in which he'd flown strike an old-growth cedar tree before the ship barrel-rolled into the mountainside. That image was the only one he focused on, stuttering and shaking all the while. Watching him was disconcerting, painful even. One of the other guys in the group got up and moved to the opposite side of the room. "Dude," he said to Max, "Your story is the most petrifying thing I've ever heard. How does your head not explode?"

Max was stuck in a flashback. He felt emotionally numb. Disconnected from reality. Since the crash, his life seemed incoherent. He was able to say, "Everything up to the crash is 20/20 in my mind. Everything after is pieces." He repeatedly heard the thundering boom of the rotor hitting the tree as his forward view totally blurred from the helicopter spiraling to the ground over and over with relentless "strapped in- the-left front seat" detail.

Traumatic memories like Max's are not the same as regular memories. Under normal circumstances, the rational (cognitive) and emotional memory systems work together to produce an integrated whole. Daily memories without much "emotional punch" fade away quickly. While cues and sensations around events, people, and things that have personal and emotional meaning to us are retrieved more readily, add adrenaline to the mix and memory crystallizes around the troublesome emotion felt at the time.

For example, a woman I knew asked me to go to lunch. I accepted, expecting a friendly conversation, or discussion of a client she wanted to refer. Instead, of a pleasant chat, she described how months before, she had enrolled in a 12-step program and reached the stage where she was supposed to make amends to the persons she had harmed. Over Pad Thai, she proceeded to list every horrible rumor she had spread about me for years in my community. And I thought we were friends! I certainly could have been happy the rest of my life without that information. I remember walking out of what had been one of my favorite restaurants physically feeling a punch to my gut and a stunned numbness in my head. Oddly enough, I don't recall the woman's name, but I'm sure I never accepted an invitation from her again and rarely go back to that restaurant. The emotional memory of embarrassment and confusion remains whereas the exact content of her remarks has faded.

Under extreme stress, terror, or inescapable horror, the emotional brain, which is not under conscious control and can't communicate verbally, takes over, and the brain areas that integrate, make sense of, and store memories go offline.

As Max tried to describe his trauma, the emotional part of his brain hijacked the rational part and strong emotions rather than words came out. Rather than describe a narrative story, the information came out in fragments of emotions, sensations, images, and sounds. Try as he might, he was not in control of this process.

These days, Max exudes command presence. He easily holds himself with a straight back and squared shoulders. He speaks in a precise manner and enunciates every word. During a conversation with him, you feel like you're the only person in the room, and if you say anything amusing, his eyes light up and he breaks into a soft laugh.

In a photo of Max after his recovery, he's wearing a bright yellow Nomex fire suit, walking calmly in front of a 50-foot wall of fire, daring it to cross the fire line. It doesn't dare. To look at that photo, you'd never know he nearly died in a chopper crash. He is one of those guys who gets to heaven by backing away from hell.

Years later, Max is still a little out of breath when he talks about the day of his incident, but otherwise, his gaze is direct and his speech precise. I can tell he wants to tell me about every moment of the crash, at least those he can remember. As he talks, I don't need to ask many questions because he is meticulous in the details. He's obviously the type of guy who's used to taking charge.

At the time of the incident, he had worked as a fire behavior analyst for a large wildland fire fighting agency for five years. According to the National Wildfire Coordinating Group (2020) a fire behavior analyst is responsible for collecting weather data, developing strategic and tactical fire behavior information, predicting fire growth, and interpreting fire characteristics for use by incident overhead. "In other words," Max said, "my job was to determine how fast fire was going, which direction it will travel, and how intense it will be when it gets there."

A large fire had been burning for several days in a mountainous area inhabited for centuries by indigenous peoples. Max was deployed to the fire along with a couple of hundred wildland firefighters, including hot shots, dozer operators, seasonal and full-time firefighters, an incident meteorologist, a resource protection officer, and helicopter crews.

The fire had not changed shape for about three days on the day that the helicopter accident occurred. One of Max's responsibilities was to regularly map the fire perimeter for the incident command team that he worked on. The incident commander on this day had asked Max to fly and get a final perimeter. Helicopters are the best operational platform for accurately mapping fire perimeters and Max had done this type of mission over one hundred times in his career. This mission would entail flying completely around the fire over the visible established fire line that separated unburned green areas from the black burned areas.

Max hadn't previously met the pilot of the helicopter on previous fires and knew nothing about his background. When he arrived at the helipad, he noted the pilot was an older gentleman with some gray in his hair. Max assumed he had a few years on the job. Later, Max discovered that the pilot had been certified to fly helicopters for only three years and had little if any high altitude, mountain experience.

This type of mapping mission is widely classified as "low and slow" because the ability to see the fire line can be quite difficult from high above the ground at faster speeds, especially when trying to find the fire underneath tree canopies. However, low and slow missions are also the most dangerous since there is little time and/or elevation for the pilot to work with if something goes wrong.

Max started to develop a slight uneasy feeling soon after arriving at the heli base after talking to some of the base personnel about the type of helicopter he was scheduled to fly in because they said this type of helicopter was not particularly well suited for "low and slow missions." However, he chose to ignore these feelings because he had grown comfortable with doing this same type of mission many times before without ever having a problem.

However, during the flight precheck, Max became even more uneasy because the weight manifest calculation was taking unusually long, but he consciously choose to ignore these feelings and just focus on the mission details that had to be accomplished.

And then the pilot said while walking to the helicopter, "Don't worry, but this take-off will be a little ugly. We're a little heavy in fuel, but once we have forward airspeed, we'll be okay." At this point, the hair on the back of Max's neck was starting to stand straight up, but Max rationalized that the pilot just had to know what he is doing professionally. He told himself, "I mean who am I to question the judgment of a licensed pilot?" Again, Max chooses to ignore his uneasy feelings that something was just not right about this upcoming flight, and he boarded the helicopter.

Max explains, "In any accident, there is not just one mistake, but a chain of events that build-up to the final crisis. Someone could intervene at any point and stop the momentum. I could have prevented this accident, but I didn't. Even though the hairs on the back of my neck were standing up, I chose to ignore my gut feelings as something not worthy to stop and listen to. I deferred to the mistaken belief that other people's judgment was inherently better than mine in all subject matters in which I was not an expert in."

During take-off, Max's anxiety finally could no longer be ignored. The helicopter was too heavy for the thin high elevation mountain air and warm air temperatures. After traveling 300 feet horizontally, they were still only six inches off the ground.

Max told the pilot, "If there's a problem, just put the ship on the ground."

The pilot kept trying for lift. "It will be fine once we have forward airspeed," he said.

Max repeated, "If there's any fucking problem, put this fucking ship on the ground."

Finally, the helicopter rose with increased airspeed and cleared nearby power lines.

Later, Max learned that the air-ops section chief had also expressed serious concern about the accuracy of the weight manifest after watching this helicopter take-off. He was going to ground the helicopter but was told that the pilot planned to burn off extra fuel and lighten the overall weight of the helicopter to safe limits before going to the fire.

But rather than burning off fuel, the pilot headed directly to the site of the fire. They were flying 400 feet above the tree line when the helicopter started to climb out of a major canyon bottom. The forward airspeed slowed as a result and the ship began what is known as "settling with power," meaning that the blades begin to stall. The result is a severe loss of lift and can lead to a high rate of descent. In other words, the helicopter began the process of falling out of the sky. This ship was going to crash if something wasn't done quick.

Within seconds, they were flying below the tree line. Max later found out that an experienced pilot would have attempted to slide sideways down the mountain to gain more airspeed at the first sign of any trouble. But instead, this pilot chose to pull back on the collective to gain more elevation as he tried to go straight up to the ridgetop and lost even more forward airspeed as a result. They were traveling 80 mph below the tree line with no landing zone in sight when the pilot said, "I think we are going to make it."

As Max related his story to me, he looked up and his voice caught a bit. He was trying to control his emotion. "At that same instant, the ship's rotor hit a cedar tree forty feet above the ground. This rotor strike instantly ripped the entire main rotor off the helicopter. The rear vertical rotor kept spinning causing the helicopter to barrel roll rapidly to the right. I leaned to my right to stay centered in the cockpit. My vision blurred and my thought processes went into slow motion.

"I thought, 'This is how I'm going to die. I am strapped into this seat, and I can't believe I'm this fucking unlucky.' I knew deep down to my very core that I was going to die. Once you experience this feeling, you can never un-know it. I was spinning onto nano-space and then instantly blacked out when the ship collided with the ground."

I asked him if he was doing okay, I didn't want to re-traumatize him by having him relive the incident.

"Really, it helps to talk about it," he says. He takes a deep breath and continues, "The helicopter crashed about 100 feet from cedar rotor strike.

In that 100-feet, the ship did a nearly complete barrel roll and crashed right side up. The skids on the bottom of the helicopter are designed to collapse on impact as a safety feature to absorb seven G-forces. Without crashing right side up, the skids would not have protected us, and everyone would have died in this crash. In other words, we had basically a 1 in 360-degree chance of survival during the one second it took for the helicopter to completely barrel roll to its eventual crash site. Not the greatest odds. I won the barrel roll lottery that afternoon.

"I woke up a few minutes later totally saturated in aviation fuel. The windows had blown out of the helicopter, and the instrument panel was resting on my legs. I simply could not in my dazed state comprehend why I did not have the ability to use my legs to kick off the instrument panel. Fortunately, the transmission had fallen away, or I might have been crushed by it."

Max's first thought was to stay in the helicopter until the rotors stopped. Then he realized there were no rotors. He struggled to get out but couldn't. Among other injuries, his left femur was totally shattered, and his L-1 vertebra was crushed. He learned later that the helicopter crashed in the "green," an unburned burned area directly in the path of a spot fire that was racing up the hill toward them. He saw that the pilot had climbed out of the helicopter and was laying on his back in pain.

Suddenly, the crash site was surrounded by firefighters. They started pulling Max out of the helicopter. He recalls asking one of them to retrieve his sunglasses and GPS. He was told, "There's no time, man."

Fourteen hundred yards below the crash site, the main fire had spotted a new fire. The spot fire crowned and began rapidly freight-training up the hill toward the crash site. There was no time to properly place the fuel-soaked Max on a backboard with full C-spine precautions. The young firefighters dropped their safety and fire equipment to quicken their pace up the hill just to stay ahead of the raging fire that was racing up to overtake them. They passed Max like a baton in a relay race 200 yards up the hill to the safe zone. He smiles, "All I remember is seeing legs running and then someone else would grab me, and then I saw more legs running," The entire crash site was burned over two minutes after they pulled Max from the downed helicopter.

His eyes mist over. "They had every right to leave me. The first priority of every firefighter is to protect themselves, then their crew, then others. Firefighters racing a fire uphill to a safe zone has never been a good bet because the fire nearly always wins. There are numerous names of deceased firefighters on memorials across the western US who have lost just this kind of race. These young men and women truly risked their lives to save mine."

As the fire raced up the hill, it incinerated the crashed helicopter, a crew bus, and a heavy-duty truck specialized to service bulldozers. The firefighters delivered Max to a medivac helicopter waiting for them at the safe zone. The ship tried to take off, but with the heavy load and the air thin from the heat and elevation, it could not get more than 10-feet off the ground. Firefighters began to take cover because they thought a second helicopter accident was just about to happen. When they could, they quickly unloaded Max just as the crown fire reached the edge of the safe zone.

Another more powerful fire agency helicopter, with greater lifting power came in with a water bucket attached. It dropped its bucket. The firefighters heaved Max into the back as flames crossed overhead. The Helitack fire captain yelled, "Go. Go. Go."

The helicopter lifted through the heat, smoke, and flames, and carried Max to safety. The Helitack captain offered to hold Max's hand until they could transfer him to the medivac ship. Max nearly crushed the captain's hand.

He recalls feeling no pain immediately after the crash. But now on the medivac flight to the hospital, the endorphins had worn off and the pain from his injuries and the aviation fuel eating away his skin had become intense. As the medics were cutting away his Nomex firefighting clothes, they asked if he wanted morphine. Max emphatically gasped, "Yes." He relaxed and fell into a blissful sleep. For the first time that day, he escaped from the supreme urgency and was able to briefly detach from the maxed-out emotional buzzing of trying to comprehend what the hell just happened and why was he still alive.

He recalls waking up to the surgeon who was going to repair his femur asking him if he was allergic to anything. Max shook his head and the surgeon said, "Sweet dreams."

After that point, Max's memory became sketchy. He was in surgery for hours. A colleague contacted his wife, and the agency arranged a flight for her to be with him. He woke up in the ICU and was overjoyed to see her. She is his rock. When his daughter came to visit for the first time, she saw that he was barely recognizable from his injuries. She burst into tears. While thankful for his family and grateful for their support, he felt crushing guilt for being a burden to them.

The hospital stay was an ordeal. His vertebra was crushed, and he wasn't allowed to twist or move in any way until his spine could be surgically repaired, which for an active guy was torture. The nurses came in every 15 to 20 minutes to roll him from one side of the bed to another with the support of pillows all the while taking great care to keep his spine stable. He was in and out of consciousness for days. He'd wake up for a few brief moments to see someone standing next to his hospital bed but would quickly fade back to sleep without ever saying goodbye. His room was extremely busy with well-wishers and his wife became overwhelmed with the implied obligation to entertain Max's visitors while he lay unconscious for extended periods of time. It was all just too much. Fortunately, he was soon assigned as his agency-family liaison and provided much-needed organizational and emotional support for his wife and kids. Max's former battalion chief has remained a close family friend ever since.

There were many surgeries, with all the inherent frustrations. Max explains, "The neurosurgeons spent significant amounts of time telling me of all the possible things that could go wrong two days in a row, as if I really had a choice about having the back surgery to repair my spine."

He hated the nasogastric tube and asked the ICU nurse to remove it. When she said it had to remain in place until the doctor ordered it to be removed, he waited until she left the room and pulled it out himself. The nurse went ballistic. As he was telling this story, he chuckled. "I've been a rule follower my entire life, but the tube was too much."

While he was adjusting to his new pain meds after his ICU morphine drip was stopped, he got behind on the pain curve. He was in agony and every second felt like hours. He was given narcotic meds and the pain went away, but in the days that followed, he became physically addicted to this very powerful opiate medication.

The nursing staff woke him every hour and eventually he started to hallucinate, which "scared the shit" out of him. Finally, his doctor ordered that he not be disturbed at night and the hallucinations stopped.

As he improved a bit, the only thing he could do was watch daytime TV, which was mind-numbing. It seemed everyone in his life had something to do or someplace to go. Life went on for them and he was stuck. He realized he was going to have to live with his injuries, mental and physical, forever. The terrifying ambiguity of whether he would ever fully recover and get his life back flooded his mind 24/7.

His eyes darkened at the memory. "The music of life suddenly stopped for me, and I was facing the strong possibility of no longer being able to do the dance that I had grown comfortable with and one that I always assumed would never change. This dance, that I worked hard to achieve, included being a firefighter capable of supporting my family, being a physically active supportive dad and husband for my family, enjoying exercise and sports, hiking, and camping, and so much more. I was faced with the likely prospect of rebuilding my life from scratch at the age of 50 and having no idea what it might look like. I began to feel very sorry for myself. This accident shattered any illusion of control that I might have ever had. I'd been an Eagle Scout. I learned growing up to always follow the rules. I told myself I would be okay if I followed the rules. But that worldview radically changed on the day of the helicopter accident by experiencing in the final seconds the unambiguous knowledge that I was going to die right there and then. I couldn't believe it. There were no more givens. My world would never be safe again."

Then, one day, he looked out the window and saw snow on the magnificent mountains that cradled the town. He recalled the good times he'd spent hiking, skiing, and spending time with his loved ones in the mountains. He imagined the clean air, the clear skies, the brilliant stars at night, the wildlife, the streams, and waterfalls. He felt some relief, a hint of joy, and realized he'd be okay.

He was discharged but his challenges were hardly over. He couldn't get into the bathtub. His mother came over daily and poured warm water on him while he stood on the back porch. "If you're handicapped, your house becomes a prison."

On one of his first outings, he went to buy shoes at JCPenney. "I was wearing the turtle shell to support my spine, and I couldn't bend over to tie my shoes. My left leg was not working at that time, and I walked incredibly slow with crutches. The shoe saleswomen looked at me like I had two heads. She clearly didn't want to deal with a handicapped person."

He discussed going off the pain meds and his physician agreed. Unwisely, he decided to go cold turkey. He describes the experience, "The first day was okay. The second day I was a little anxious. The night tremors from narcotic withdrawal started with a vengeance on the third night. It was unbelievable. I had to put a towel in my mouth to keep my teeth from breaking because every part of my body was shaking so bad. After three nights, I finally went to the ER, and they told me to taper down slowly. I tried again a second time by tapering down as instructed but the same thing happened. I ultimately needed special medicine to also suppress the night shakes before I could end my physical addiction to narcotics. Being addicted is a terrifying thing."

He wanted to return to work. "I clearly remember walking down the street with my cane when my fire engine with my crew traveled right past me going Code 3. I truly hated my cane and everything it represented. I thought when I got rid of my cane that I could go back to work. However, I just could not magically speed up the healing process and end the haunting ambiguity of not knowing how my future would unfold. At that point, I couldn't take care of myself physically or mentally by myself without the help of others. This was intuitively wrong because firefighters are supposed to be strong and only help others. I feared I'd never go back." He qualified for disability, but the loss of overtime severely impacted his income, and he had to refinance his home.

Then there were the memory problems. During the crash, Max suffered a contrecoup traumatic brain injury. This occurred when his skull hit the metal surfaces in the helicopter and his brain was bounced around in his skull during the crash, bruising it. Max had always had a great memory and the injury caused a loss of vocabulary and even recognition of people he knew well. "It was maddening to have a clearly defined thought only to stop the mid-sentence in a discussion because I no longer had an adequate vocabulary to express it."

He became emotional. He was so enraged at the pilot that he "could have disemboweled him with a plastic spoon." He ruminated about the incident. "I was also supremely angry at myself. I told myself the flight would be okay even though I ignored the hair on the back of my neck that was standing up telling me something was wrong. I tell my trainees, 'If you feel something is off, even if you can't put words to it, then stop until you can, no matter what else is happening.' I carried shame and guilt for a long time because on that day I was too mission-driven to give proper reverence to my inner voice and forgot that I alone am the one primarily responsible for my own safety.

"We as firefighters work in an extremely dangerous environment and our specialized training helps greatly to mitigate that risk. One cannot let fear overtake you or the mission of protecting life, property and the environment would never get accomplished. Then again, firefighting is not like soldiers fighting in war because there is no such thing as expendable losses. At the end of the shift, all firefighters need to be able to go home to their families. Trusting one's own inner voice is key towards saving your own skin, and that is exactly what I did wrong due to my tunnel vision in trying to accomplish my mapping assignment. An assignment that I had successfully done without incident well over a hundred times before."

Although his physical body was slowly recovering, the PTSD symptoms came on with a vengeance. "I kept re-experiencing the three seconds of terror spinning in the fucking ship knowing I was going to die. I'd break down into tears ten times a day. I felt absolutely crazy."

A fellow firefighter recommended the West Coast Posttrauma Retreat. Max was accepted into the program. He arrived shaking and crying and barely able to speak. "I recall that I cried my eyes out all week. The therapist did EMDR (Eye Movement Desensitization Reprocessing) on me several times. The last time the shaking and crying finally stopped. It was a miracle. It was the beginning of when I began to get better.

"I also had a lot to learn about the concept of forgiveness while at WCPR because I had too many common misconceptions about what it was. Forgiveness has nothing to do with granting absolution to the other offending party. In fact, it has little or nothing to do with the person who may have wronged you. It is a 'process of letting go' of past grievances so that I am no longer carrying within me the all-consuming anger that can serve no other purpose than to poison my life going forward. I had to learn to let go of the pilot, and most of all, I had to learn to let go of what I did as well if I ever wanted to fully recover.

"The other thing was that my therapist at WCPR was involved in the post-crash CISM (critical incident stress management) that took place when I was in the hospital. The therapist had dozens of details about the responses and reactions of the other firefighter that I didn't know. Putting it all together helped me connect the dots and make a narrative I could understand at an intellectual level. It was immensely helpful."

Less than a year later, after Max was well enough, he returned to work as a fire captain at his old station. He was tremendously humbled because he knew of other firefighters with severe burns or permanent spinal injuries who were not so lucky. Five years later he accepted a position teaching at the fire academy. Three years later, he rose to a high rank in his organization and helped to build a mental health program for fire employees that included CISM and support for firefighters emotionally impacted by critical incidents. If anything, the accident seemed to fuel his productivity and service to others.

Ten years after the accident, he finally decided to retire but found that he had an identity crisis. If he was no longer a firefighter, then who was he? This was the very same crisis that he so desperately tried to avoid in the months of recovery following his accident when his future seemed so uncertain. Then, one night just a few months after retiring this reality, came back to face him head-on.

At 2 a.m., he heard someone banging on his door. It was a neighborhood girl. Her home was on fire, and she was panicked. Max responded out of the house in his pajamas and made sure everyone was out of her house. Then he evacuated the adjacent neighbors. By the time the fire engines arrived, he had the familiar feeling of authority and control. Then as the firefighters attacked the fire, he realized they were making some significant tactical errors, pushing the fire into the house rather than out among others. "I was thinking, 'Are you guys serious?'" he said. "I used to teach this stuff at the fire academy. I wanted to correct them, educate them, teach them how to do it right."

Suddenly, I realized I was just an old guy standing there in my pajamas. Those young firefighters looked right through me. They. Did. Not. Care. My attitude had to change."

To find himself, he realized he had to start looking within.

A close friend and his wife both suggested he seek therapy. He thought about it for a while and remembered that when he was at WCPR, he realized for the first time that both of his parents were alcoholics. He decided to take a quiz about the traits of adult children of alcoholics. "I scored 16 of 18 traits. It's very difficult to diagnose self-deception by yourself," he explains. That realization became a touchstone and ultimately, he ended up in an Adult Children of Alcoholics group.

First responders can do their jobs only if they maintain an attitude of confident cockiness. When a tragedy is completely out of their control, they resort to self-blame and magical thinking. These types of self-criticism, even when a call goes sideways through no fault of their own, allow them the belief they can control circumstances to avoid tragedy. Self-reproach is almost universal in first responders. Max's story delineates the difference between the type of rumination that motivates a first responder to improve, or alternately can destroy their lives. For example, rehashing a call and trying to figure out how it could have gone better can be a healthy learning moment. Blaming oneself unrealistically for things out of one's control can be destructive. Max's tendency to be overly self-critical likely began in childhood when he was trying to earn his dad's approval and love, and as such, the internal drive towards perfection began, an impossible and incredibly self-destructive belief.

"On the surface, I had a 'Leave it to Beaver' childhood. We'd play outdoors, riding our bikes up and down the street until dinnertime, and then do homework. Basically, all I wanted was to be a good kid and to be loved and accepted."

After some self-examination, he realized he grew up in a time when the father was the head of the house and expected the rest of the family to bend to his will. His father worked hard, came home at the end of the day in time for cocktail hour, and every evening without fail consumed significant amounts of alcohol with my mom. As a child, I had no other reference and assumed that this type of behavior was entirely normal.

Max recalls, "Although there were no outward signs of obvious abuse, now, with the aid of perfect hindsight, most of the typical alcoholic controlling behaviors were certainly present during my childhood. I knew that my grandfather was a mean alcoholic from witnessing his abusive outbursts at nearly all family holiday dinners. My dad in retrospect was not an overtly mean person. In fact, he could be quite kind and caring at times. I always knew that my dad loved me, and I certainly loved my dad. But anyone who challenged his authority within our family even slightly received his verbal wrath. My mom was a frequent target of this wrath. He did not yell or scream or shout obscenities. However, the intensity and inflection in his voice as well as his choice of words were highly critical and scary. I strongly identified every time with my mom when she was the target of his anger. In looking back at my youth, I was not allowed to have any boundaries with my dad that he did not approve of. Unfortunately, as a result, I learned growing up to have little or no boundaries with authority figures in my life. I learned to follow the rules and avoid conflict as best I can."

His father would withhold acknowledgment and praise of any of Max's extracurricular activities if they did not match up with his priorities. He had no energy whatsoever to attend any of his games in high school or college. Because of this and his early difficulties learning how to read, Max slowly came to believe that he was just not good enough.

Max continued, "I've been chasing my father's approval and love for my entire life. My father always regretted not achieving the rank of Eagle Scout and liked to say he lived vicariously through the achievements of his two sons. But this declaration only pertained to the achievements that he wanted us to pursue, not the ones we would choose for ourselves on our own.

"I joined the Boy Scouts, and this was a truly wonderful and integral part of my life as a teen up until I started college. I learned how to camp, hike, and many mountaineering skills that I would thoroughly enjoy for the rest of my life as well as the opportunity to develop leadership skills from some truly great adults in the program.

"The higher I climbed towards the rank of Eagle Scout, the more my dad paid increasing amounts of attention to me. Becoming an Eagle Scout was truly a very proud moment in my life but more importantly, my dad demonstrably showed real unabashed joy and approval in my achievement. And while this was indeed a very special moment for me, I also learned that perfection and achievement could bring with them love and acceptance. If you have grown up feeling less than as a child, then the behavior of chasing perfection and proving yourself to others to gain acceptance can be a drug. But this euphoric feeling rarely lasted very long before I was quickly moving on to my next quest. The innate concept that I had any value as a person or that I was worthy just because I existed was completely foreign to me."

I asked Max when he realized his former self had turned the corner, the figurative death and rebirth of the hero.

He said, "The West Coast Posttrauma Retreat saved my life, but when I went through the steps at Al-Anon, I realized I was too focused on pleasing the alcoholic, my father, and not taking responsibility for my personal growth and self-care. For much of my life, it was too easy to go back to behaviors I learned as a child that no longer served me when I was stressed. At WCPR I observed that everyone would say that they wanted to get well but many just didn't want to do the work. You can't go around your emotional shit in your life. There are no shortcuts. You have to work your way through your emotional shit to ultimately find recovery.

"I spent 20 years in an unhappy marriage because I did not want to be a failure, especially in the eyes of my dad. I say that because I just assumed to know what my dad might be thinking but never actually talked to him about my unhappy marriage. Basing my choices on seeking the approval of others is never a healthy behavior. After he died, I left that relationship and found my wife. Before, I used relationships to feel better. Now I feel better within myself.

"Once I realized I needed to take care of my life, not my father's, it was the beginning of a new life for me. I discovered that I wasn't broken. I didn't need to feel ashamed or less than just because I was not perfect. In fact, I found that it is our imperfections that indeed make us loveable and more relatable. Holding on to my shame and resentment was a choice that I was no longer willing to make. To no longer blame anyone else for the results of my choices brought me incredible freedom because I no longer wanted to remain stuck as a victim. My parents were not perfect, but they truly did the best they could to raise me."

He has also become a sponsor for Adult Children of Alcoholics. He had found that teaching and supporting others gives him a sense of purpose. "I sponsor people because I learned the hard way that diagnosing self-deception is very difficult by yourself." He paused for a moment and looked into my eyes. "I realized as the adult child of alcoholics I gave my power to others even before the accident, so in a way, the crash was partially my fault because I accommodated the pilot and didn't insist on putting the helicopter down even though my gut was screaming to."

"What other kinds of growth have you noticed?" I asked.

He smiled. "I'm agnostic, and I'm not sure if or how God fits into my life, but I learned that my higher power can be the best within me if I am patient and quiet enough to listen."

Max also finds peace in the hours he spends every week hiking the picturesque mountains in his community. Although he has always been comfortable in nature, his appreciation of the untamed waters and verdant forests is deeper than ever. It's an enduring relationship given that after the crash, it was the view of the snow-capped Cascades that gave him joy during the darkest time in the hospital. To him, the mountains represent hope and life. He has enrolled in college classes. He journals. The focus of his recovery is now "to enjoy the present, not regret the past, nor fear the future.

"I still have ups and downs," he continues. "I still want to please others to my detriment. For example, I was called to jury duty. Despite the fact I'm very uncomfortable sitting, I wanted to be the good citizen and follow the rules, so I showed up." He laughs. "And I caught COVID there. Another lesson."

"I continue to have pain and will need more surgeries. Occasionally, I get triggered, but for the most part, my PTSD is in remission. It's a paradox. You can't live life like it's unsafe, even if it is, but you also have to listen to your instincts to avoid danger. Oddly enough, my new strength is to realize I'm not in control of everything."

"So, there it is," I said. "You have grown immensely since the crash. You're more connected spiritually and to nature, you have a new purpose in helping others, and you're closer to your loved ones."

Max looks at me warmly. His eyes, face, his body are serene. "The helicopter accident was the best thing that ever happened to me because I would have never grown otherwise." He smiles and chuckles. "When the student is ready, the teacher will be provided."

There is a heartbreaking finale to Max's story. A couple of months after I last visited with him, he was diagnosed with a terminal brain tumor, the kind that takes life away in weeks. Max died even before his wife could notify most people of his illness. His Celebration of Life took place in a nature park, surrounded by water and mountains, with his friends and loved ones, exactly as he would have wanted it. As a chorus of women sang to honor his life, dozens of geese began to honk in unison as if to welcome Max home. The experience was transcendent, especially considering Max professed skepticism about God.

After I met Max the first time, he called me his angel. I guess now he is mine. Here's to peace wherever you are.

CHAPTER 4

VICTOR

Multi-Casualty Incident

"There is no present or future. Only the past happening over and over again now."
EUGENE O'NEILL

"Traumatic stress is an illness of not being able to be fully alive in the present."
PIERRE JANET, 1889

If you were hiking in the woods and Victor emerged from behind a giant redwood, you might well mistake him for Paul Bunyon. He's a little less than six feet four, built like a brick wall, and sports a thick beard worthy of—well—Paul Bunyon. He typically wears a plaid shirt, red being the preferred color, and hiking boots tough enough to tame the most rugged, steep, volcanic rock of the Cascade Mountain range. He always carries a chain saw, a wrench, a car jack, a shovel, or some essential tool in his hand. He can fix any machine put in front of him and build any structure you could come up with. He's the guy you would want to be friends with when the apocalypse comes.

Victor's love was fighting wildfire. He was proud to say he served with a large government agency for more than ten years. Wildland firefighters aren't the same as the rest of us. They work 16-hour days for weeks or sometimes months at a time, with no breaks, in filthy, ungodly hot conditions. Before being hired, they are expected to hike straight up a three-mile mountain, wearing sweltering Nomex suits, carrying a 45-pound pack, in 45 minutes. And they never complain. In fact, they consider themselves to have the best career on earth.

Victor's apocalypse began at the end of a long day after fighting fire at 6000 feet on one of the most remote mountaintops in the Cascades. Radio communication was sketchy and cell phone coverage was out of the question. Victor and his crew were winding down from fighting fire. Some were about to be ferried back to base camp; the rest—30 or so firefighters and support personnel—planned to pitch camp on the mountain for the night.

The firefighting helicopter, a Sikorsky S-61, had just returned from ferrying 13 firefighters back to the base camp. A thunder and lightning storm was approaching, and there was some urgency to get 13 additional firefighters off the mountain.

Victor's final job for the night was to clear the Sikorsky helicopter transporting the rest of the firefighters, crew, and equipment off the mountain. After a safety briefing, he cleared the chopper, waved at his friends, and turned to walk back to camp. As the process progressed, he jotted in his journal, "H 44. 1935. 766 down." The time was 7:45 p.m.

The sound of the engine straining got his attention. Later, he said it sounded like it was sucking for fuel. He turned and saw the chopper struggling to lift. It was no more than a few hundred feet above the ground and had traveled 150 yards from the landing zone.

Involuntarily, Victor held his breath and prayed for the chopper to clear the trees. Then, in what seemed like a slow-motion video, the six-ton chopper sank almost peacefully into the vegetation. Whack. Whack. Whack. Propellers shredded tree limbs. Ten firefighters, three crewmembers, and all their heavy gear and firefighting equipment crashed into the forest. Gas exploded with a loud woof. The chopper rolled to the side. Flames shot out from everywhere. A fireball filled the sky. A blast of overheated air scalded Victor's face. Wood chips and pieces of metal pummeled his body. A hunk of a tree flew by. Hot hydraulic fluid shot past him. He couldn't move for a moment. He couldn't believe his senses. The crash was over before he could blink.

His flight instinct kicked in and he ran for his life. He recalls running at an angle to escape the debris from the blast. Popping sounds—in his mind's eye, he imagined the bodies of his friends blowing up. He took cover and waited for the moving parts to stop. There was nothing else to do. It was completely out of his control.

The blast blew the copilot out of the chopper. Victor ran to him and saw his flesh melting off. There was nothing to do for him. Victor put his cell phone on the copilot's chest "for comfort." A silly thought, but the only thing he could think of.

Then he looked around. He could barely take in the scene. The helicopter was burning. There was no possibility of rescuing anyone from the fiery carcass. In the fading light, his crew searched for survivors while he remained on incident command. Three others besides the copilot had been thrown out but not much could be done to attend to their serious injuries. Ultimately, the pilot-in-command, the safety crewmember, and seven firefighters were fatally injured.

Victor and his remaining crew stayed on the mountain that night because there was no means to get off it. Sleep was out of the question. He rested behind a rock, but the smells of aviation fuel and his friends' bodies burning unnerved him.

That night, Victor believed he heard the ghosts of the dead calling to him. He walked to the ashes to visit them, to commune silently with them.

He went over and over the manifest ruminating about where he could have screwed up in his payload calculations. "Hike to H43." He recalled that he had given the helicopter crew a safety briefing right before it took off. He wondered, "How effective was I?"

Not until 10 a.m. that morning did another helicopter arrive to take Victor and his remaining crew out.

He was given four days off work to recover from the ordeal. The time was completely inadequate for healing. His agency commended him for "stepping up in the face of duty—kind of like a purple heart," he explained.

That didn't stop the continual nightmares and "daymares," anxiety, and waves of terror. He couldn't wipe the images of the crash scene from his mind's eye. Wherever he went, whatever he did, the images stayed right in front of his face 24/7. He couldn't close his eyes or open them without the vision of the crash appearing directly in front of his eyes. The images wouldn't go away. He was stuck in a flashback of the most horrific type.

Victor's intrusive images were extremely distressing. He's a guy who expects to have mastery over his body. He can move when he wants to and stop when he decides to. Even when his reflexes take over in an emergency, he expects to regain control quickly. He expects to have command over his arms and legs and every other part. That's how he's survived the challenges he faced in his career as a wildland firefighter, and for that matter, everyday functioning like driving a truck or picking up milk at the store.

Imagine how it would feel to have no control over your mind. Horrific images just pop up in front of your eyes for apparently no reason. Or memories that caused actual physical pain and make you want to die just to make them stop. And terrible feelings of guilt that crush your soul. Sleeping is impossible—your body seems to think there's a velociraptor outside your door waiting to attack you. That's what PTSD feels like. You can't control it and it never goes away. You relive the event, day and night. And try as you might, you can't distract yourself or talk yourself down.

Victor tried distracting himself with alcohol and found there wasn't enough of it on earth to block out the images. He couldn't work hard enough, piss people off enough, rage at his girlfriend enough to make himself sleep through the night without startling awake in the middle of the landing zone, drenched in sweat, heart pounding out of his chest. He felt crazy and ashamed. He didn't talk to his friends about it, even those in his crew who had also witnessed the crash. It was just too painful.

Research about how involuntary recollections develop after trauma in humans is difficult because scientists can't generally stand around waiting for someone to experience a trauma then whisk them to an fMRI machine to measure activity in different parts of the brain. In addition, obtaining an exact measurement or definition of involuntary recollections is difficult in a laboratory because people with PTSD experience various intensities, frequencies, and durations of involuntary recollections. However, research has shown that these recollections almost certainly involve parts of the brain that involve memory, emotion, and executive control.

Bessel van der Kolk (2014, pp.69-73) studied a couple who had developed PTSD after being involved in an auto accident and agreed to have their brains scanned by an fMRI before entering treatment. The idea was to recreate the functioning of their brains as they had been during the accident.

The husband "Stan" went into a flashback and relived the trauma of being trapped inside his car. The fMRI showed that his amygdala, a part of the emotional brain also called "the smoke detector," lit up. In the case of a threat, the amygdala sends a message to the hypothalamus triggering nervous system responses and stress hormones, such as adrenaline and cortisol, that prepare the body for fight or flight. The amygdala doesn't understand time, and when activated, it makes the experience seem in the present moment. Stan's amygdala made him feel like the crash was still happening.

The dorsolateral prefrontal cortex (DLPRC), also called the time-keeper, gives a sense of past, present, and future and is part of the executive part of the brain. Stan's was deactivated, indicating he lost his sense of time and was trapped in the moment, perceiving that it would go on forever.

Another part of Stan's brain that went offline during the crash was his thalamus, which, under normal circumstances, acts as a gatekeeper, gathering information from the eyes, ears, and skin, and integrating them into our autobiographical memory. However, in trauma, the thalamus malfunctions, and information is not integrated, which explains why traumatic memories are recalled as isolated images, sounds, and sensations accompanied by intense emotions rather than the narrative of regular memories. Like Stan, people with PTSD have no filter. They are on constant overload and can't negotiate life without isolating or shutting down.

As a clinician who has treated hundreds of individuals suffering from PTSD, I can say these persistent, distressing images are not uncommon after traumatic events. In some people, they fade after a few days; some are tormented by them for years. Victor's symptoms were like those of Stan in van der Kolk's study and I imagine each of the men was feeling the same terror, shame, confusion, and embarrassment.

As the weeks went on, there were firefighter funerals. Too many funerals. And a giant memorial ceremony.

It was hell.

Victor tried to work for a while but felt ill and lost his motivation. The only way he could get to sleep was to drink. He drank to quiet his mind and numb his brain. Still, he startled awake every night drenched with sweat, still watching the crash.

In the months following, Victor found out a check pilot was on the flight. A check pilot rides along to certify that the pilot knows how to perform essential tasks such as water bucket drops, repelling, aerial ignition, and managing external loads. Victor had not been informed. That was another 200 pounds on the flight.

He began to spiral down. Then a preliminary investigation indicated the payload on the helicopter was overweight by 1000 pounds. The insinuation was that Victor, who signed off on the flight manifest, had made a mistake, although he was sure his calculations on the day of the crash were well under the weight limits. He always checked things twice on the computer, not in his head. He became demoralized and obsessed with guilt that he was at fault. He suspected that something was wrong, but what?

Over time, he wished he wished he would get fired to end the pain. He tried to get specialized treatment for PTSD, but his agency refused to pay for it and seemed to hold counseling against him, telling him he needed to go to therapy on his days off. His supervisors started examining everything he did, testing his urine and giving him a breathalyzer for alcohol. He was found positive for marijuana, but there was no offer to help him.

Finally, he couldn't make it into work anymore without being triggered. He spent his days in a numb haze "like I'm not even there" and his nights feeling out of his body, hovering over the crash site, looking down at the bodies of his friends. A strange metallic smell like burning metal was ever-present. He wondered if he was hallucinating. He was living in a continual flashback and couldn't function.

His life took another turn when he was arrested for DUI and lost his driver's license meaning he couldn't drive a fire engine.

His relationship with his girlfriend dissolved into constant fighting and he asked her to leave. The only thing that made him want to keep breathing was his love for the daughter they shared.

Finally, he was fired and told he couldn't work for five years. He lost all his hard-won qualifications—fire investigator, prevention officer, helicopter rappeler, squad boss, IC trainee, airbase radio, take-off and landing coordinator, and training.

His agency betrayed and abandoned him. He dedicated his whole career to them for nothing. He wondered if giving information to the National Transportation Safety Board was a motive for firing him. "They knew it was over-grossed," he said. "I was there the day the chopper was delivered, and I asked questions about the aircraft's capability. I said all the extra electronics, seats, padding would weigh more than the chopper could lift. The agency shushed me and said it was handled. They signed off on it anyway."

Sometime after the crash, Victor's daughter developed an infection. He called the local hospital and asked for advice. When the nurse advised that she couldn't give advice over the phone, he blew up and threatened, "I going to come down there, blow the hospital up, and set it on fire." The nurse called law enforcement who responded to Victor's house. He became combative and was arrested.

A few days in jail allowed Victor to dry out. When he finally arranged bail, he had hit his bottom. He realized he had to stop drinking or he would lose custody of his daughter.

His troubles were not over. He tried to work at a fire equipment company but found himself erupting in anger at co-workers. He couldn't afford his mortgage payment and his house was put up for auction. Various investigators repeatedly contacted him about his actions on the day of the crash. His nightmares continued, and during the days, he flashed on images of wood chips and helicopter parts flying into his face.

His self-recriminations and guilt for not doing more to save the people who died gave way to anger. He had done his job, gone above and beyond even. Why couldn't the fire service do their job? He experienced administrative and organizational, or bureaucratic betrayal.

He thought about his relationship with his father. "I always knocked myself out to get his attention and only occasionally would he throw me a bone. Like the fire service, he was clueless." He recalled that his father was absent and left him to learn about life on his own.

Therapists often ask first responders what gave the critical incident so much power? In Victor's case, his unrequited need for attention and approval from his father set him up to devote his time, energy, and in some sense his soul to the fire service. It became the family he never had, the source of his self-esteem, his purpose in life. However, in his time of need after the crash, they seemed to abandon him like his father had, and they investigated him for wrongdoing. This organizational abandonment and betrayal are commonly not only fatal to a career, but at times to first responders themselves in the form of alcohol abuse, self-destructive behaviors, and even suicide.

As Victor practiced his sobriety, he started to have good days. He found a house to rent and enjoyed time volunteering at his daughter's school. He was nominated for a leadership position.

One night, he had a dream that a lightning strike ignited a tree and started a forest fire. In the dream, he was able to able to save himself from the fire. "It was a strange dream," he said. "But it made me feel better for some reason."

He found work cutting wood and became interested in forest resource conservation. The triggers were fewer and when the anniversary of the crash came around, he almost forgot about it. With a twinge of guilt, he decided not to attend the memorial for the victims of the crash. His life was improving. Why be triggered with memories?

He was doing so well that he decided he could have a few beers. Then a few more. Then some whiskey. After a few weeks of drinking, he became depressed and had trouble sleeping. Again, he felt "stuck in space." He dreamt of burning bodies, charred and blackened skin stretched over the pink of a mouth. When the local paper ran an opinion piece about the culpability of the fire service in the helicopter crash, he thought they were blaming him personally.

He tried an antidepressant, which gave him the energy to find a seasonal captain's job training recruits at a private fire prevention service. He enjoyed the intellectual stimulation of working with new trainees. He noted, "You learn 70% of what you teach and nothing of what someone teaches you." He worked a few fires and saved some lives, which gave him confidence and motivation. He managed to pay off debts he'd accrued during his unemployment. There were ups and downs, triggers, and some nightmares, but he was coping.

One day, his trainees were not paying attention when a helicopter suddenly made a rapid descent right over him. He yelled at the crew, "Boots, not roots. Look at them so you can move!" That night he couldn't sleep. The safety issues were glaring, and he couldn't live with himself if something else happened. The trigger was so intense he knew he couldn't work fire anymore. He feared another tragedy and essentially packed up and left. He said, "That chopper crash destroyed my life."

Months later, while he was shopping for groceries, he ran into a fellow firefighter who was on scene at the crash. "We talked, really talked for the first time. And we hugged like it really mattered." A turning point. That night he had a dream of the chopper rotors "thwuping" and the engine searching for fuel right after the crash but before the explosion. However, the dream wasn't as terrifying as before, and the visions started to fade from vivid color to black and white and they began to move from right in front of his eyes to farther away and to the side of his head.

Several years post-crash, he stopped drinking again. Instead of sitting at home bored, he decided to go out and do things. He started having a mental vision of looking inside the chopper and seeing his friends in ashes, but the emotional punch of the memory was much less than before.

Then, for no reason, his brain seemed to go on overdrive again. He had a nightmare of the crew trying to get out of the falling chopper. He heard frantic thumping as they hit the sides of the cabin. Suddenly there was a cloud of toxic fumes. The crew breathed it in and "that was it for them. They died right away."

In psychotherapy, he processed the dream by using EMDR. He felt helpless, anxious, terrified, as though he were still in the middle of the scene. He thought that he failed. He couldn't find the extraction kit. People were yelling for help. Through processing, he came to believe that he did his job, and no matter what, he couldn't have saved them. In the end, he wanted peace with the incident. In his mind's eye, he was able to float above it and look down from above.

Later, he had another dream that he was observing a helicopter land on a building. It started spinning and crashed into the building causing a huge fire. However, unlike the crash on the mountain, in his dream, he managed to get everyone out. Thereafter, the nightmares lost their power. When a newspaper article or television show mentioned the crash, he might have a bad night, but he'd find a friend to talk to and it feel better.

As the months went on, his symptoms became more manageable. His disability claim was accepted so he could pay his bills. The investigation into the crash continued.

After some years of investigation, the interviews with firefighters who witnessed the accident concluded. They consistently reported that the helicopter lifted off slower than they would have expected before striking trees and crashing more than 100 yards from the lift-off point.

The final report determined that the failure of flight crewmembers to address issues related to operating the helicopter at its maximum performance capability contributed to the accident. The fatalities and survivors' injuries were caused by the immediate and intense fire that resulted from fuel spillage from the fuel tanks that were not crash-resistant, the separation from the floor of the cabin seats that were not crash-resistant, and the use of an inappropriate mechanism on the cabin seat restraints. The pilot-in-command, the safety crewmember, and seven firefighters were fatally injured; the copilot and three firefighters were seriously injured.

Ultimately, two employees of the helicopter company were convicted of falsifying performance charts and weight and balance records to win a government contract. The false information was given to pilots who calculated maximum payload capacity during firefighting operations.

Victor was in no way culpable. The fact that he suffered for years not only from trauma, but from abandonment, is beyond tragic. He celebrated the findings by taking his daughter to San Diego.

First responders believe the world is fair, and that their training and competency will protect them. They will fight to survive any adversity as long as the department has their back. When their trust is misplaced, the development of PTSD is common. Victor's story followed the psychological aftermath of a disaster in which he was not only abandoned by the department but scapegoated for political expediency.

Eleven years later, he still replays the crash in his mind, but it's not so overwhelming. "It ain't going away." He's on retirement disability and could receive a pension and social security in a few years. But he'd like to go back to work and is trying to find the motivation. He's angry that his daughter can't say my dad works on helicopters anymore. "I have to acknowledge these thoughts, or they stay stuck in my mind."

"It was a life-changing event that made me realize I wanted more out of life. I didn't want to be that guy rotting under the bridge. I had to pull myself out of it. I don't know what the click was. I had the tools, but I had to decide for myself. I wanted my kid to be proud of me and I wasn't going to rip her off from being a good dad."

Victor's journey was long and difficult. Before the crash, he was a firefighter's firefighter, an action hero. The crash threw him into a terrifying world in which he lost control of his mind, and knowledge that he was competent and in control, and his ability to work. He became chronically enraged, triggered at the slightest affront, and helpless to impede the emotional hemorrhaging caused by flashbacks. He became isolated and ashamed to talk to those closest to him about his experience. He saw himself as a failure and thought he was at fault for the crash. He felt rejected and abandoned by the agency that he devoted his life to. And he ruminated constantly about all of it.

When I think of Victor, I think of a man clawing his way to the top of a mountain. The only way to restore himself was to conquer that mountain and to make peace with it. He did it by accepting allies and mentors who could help him, by accepting his vulnerability, by looking to his past, and by having the courage to discard his emotional paralysis. He seized the sword of self-knowledge and realized that, while he is no longer a firefighter, he is still a man, a father, a provider, and a hero to those who are important.

He certainly has experienced posttraumatic growth. He has a greater appreciation of nature and conservation thereof. He has become emotionally closer to his daughter. He is more understanding of himself and forgiving of his foibles. And he doesn't talk about it, but he has an aura of connectedness to the transcendental world. He is not the same as he was before the crash, but he is better.

CHAPTER 5

SONNY

Wounding or Killing an Innocent Person

"Where there is anger, there is pain underneath."
ECKART TOLLE

Sonny is tall and sturdily built. His body exudes calm, quiet control. He maintains steady and open eye contact. When he first sees you, his eyes sparkle, and if he happens to share an amusing story his chuckle is totally infectious. While he is warm, open, candid, and eager to share his story, as he recalls heartbreaking events, his expression becomes serious, almost vulnerable and the light in his eyes dims. Throughout his narrative, even as his voice reflects his pain, he maintains a professional demeanor.

As Sonny's hero's journey of healing began, one of the first things he discovered about himself was that harsh early experiences from his childhood shaped his compassion for others, especially children. Tragically, the critical incident that started the beginning of the end of his career involved the inadvertent death of a teen at his hands.

I am familiar with the pain he feels about his critical incident, so I ask Sonny to tell me about his early childhood first. The lines in his thoughtful face seem to deepen. He is the youngest child in his family. His mother was a Southern Baptist and had rigid moral standards—no alcohol, no dancing, no sex before marriage. Although she could be judgmental, she babied Sonny and favored him over her other children. He tried to live up to her expectations and came to believe that if didn't live life the right way, he would end up in hell.

When he was three, after his parents divorced, his mother devoted herself to her children and never remarried. His father moved away and remarried a woman with older children. Sonny longed for a connection with his father and was happy when he was invited to spend the summer with him.

His joy soon turned to sadness and confusion when his older stepbrothers began to torment and bully him. His father would come home from long hours at work and hit the bottle, only to be assailed by Sonny's stepmother complaining about the boy's behavior. His father would pull off his belt and take Sonny into the back bedroom. Without listening to his side of the story, his father beat him. It wasn't long before Sonny came to believe that his father loved his new family more. He felt abandoned and alone.

After one visit, he returned to his mother's house covered in bruises. His mother took him to the police station. He was too scared to explain what his father had done. He didn't want to stop seeing him—he just wanted the beatings to stop. At the station, two seasoned gruff cops appeared and demanded he take off his clothes to show them his body. Sonny was humiliated. He screamed and cried and refused to cooperate. Interview over. Case closed.

The visits to his father stopped abruptly. His mother never explained the reason, but Sonny heard her rage on the phone at his father. Sonny believed her anger was his fault—like he'd done something wrong. After his mother cut off visitations with his father, Sonny was not invited to family events or receive birthday cards from his father. He felt lonely and sad and confused.

When he was ten, he was befriended by a teenage boy, Joey. Sonny thought that Joey really cared for him. They constructed forts and went on adventures into homeless camps where they found porn magazines. For Sonny, who had never seen a female body naked, looking at them was a big deal.

One day, Joey told Sonny to "please" him or else he wouldn't be friends anymore. He wanted Sonny to perform oral sex. Later, Sonny realized Joey had been grooming him for months, but at the time he was afraid of losing the only close relationship he had. The act was completely against Sonny's strict religious upbringing and made him feel grossed out, ashamed, dirty, and revolted. But Joey insisted, and Sonny complied. Sonny focused on the power lines overhead and tried not to gag. It was another betrayal, perhaps the most significant one in his young life. The hollow visceral feeling of being unprotected and vulnerable stayed with him for years.

While initially, Sonny had been a good student in grade school and enrolled in gifted classes, as the multiple traumas stalked him, emotional pain began to overwhelm him. He ate compulsively, gained weight, and became increasingly passive and withdrawn. Other kids began to bully him. In his junior year, he stopped seeing the sense in life and dropped out of school.

Adrift emotionally throughout his young adulthood, he eventually fell in love with an older married woman. She promised to leave her husband and finally did—for another man. Another abandonment. His discomfort around people in general, and women in particular, grew. The judgmental aspects of his fundamentalist upbringing didn't help his low self-confidence.

He longed for connection and tried once more to reach out to his father. A difficult, tenuous relationship was established. Sonny never felt comfortable enough to discuss the abuse, or the difficulties he faced in his childhood and young adulthood. And still, it was clear to Sonny that his father favored his stepmother and stepbrothers. He remained resentful and confused.

In his 20s, his life changed. He met a police sergeant who saw something valuable in him and encouraged him to apply for a job as a police officer. He did so on a whim. "I was young and dumb, but the money and benefits were good." Sonny began to pull himself up with the help of his mentor. He was happy with the job, but over the next ten years, he worked graveyards, ate junk food, and eventually reached 300 pounds. Although this self-destructive habit continued, he was able to help people in need. There were hard calls, and Sonny's sensitive nature took a beating, but he loved his job and the good things he could do. Then the series of horrible, work-related incidents began.

One evening, Sonny and his partner responded to a vehicular accident between two drunks. He found a man in the road, still breathing. He kneeled down and cradled the man's head to provide comfort. An EMT arrived on scene and told Sonny to move back. As he drew his hands away, parts of the man's head came off. He felt disgusted, dazed, and unsure of what happened. He began having trouble breathing and went to sit in his car. His sergeant sent him home. No one talked to him about it later.

Not long after, he responded to a baby who wasn't breathing. He initiated CPR and kept doing it even after the EMTs arrived and placed the baby was placed in the ambulance. At the hospital, the ER doc pronounced the baby dead. He had been strangled. No amount of CPR could have revived him. Sonny flashed on a past image of the way he'd been treated as a child and began to cry. He went to the sergeant on the peer support team and was told to get over it. Again, he received no support.

Incidents accumulated and plagued him. An officer-involved shooting of a teenager holding a knife was portrayed by the media as an execution by police. Three officers in his department took medical retirement.

An inebriated male broke into offices and threatened the officers who arrived. After one officer shot him, other officers ridiculed the shooter. He was forced to retire.

A man killed his entire family and lay in wait for law enforcement to arrive. During the confrontation, the man shot one of Sonny's colleagues.

The stress was taking its toll. Sonny was diagnosed with type 2 diabetes and high blood pressure. He minimized the diagnoses and did nothing to alter his unhealthy coping mechanism.

Soon after came the incident that killed his career. He and his squad were celebrating a drug bust at a Mexican restaurant. A call came in about a fight with broken bottles. Sonny's partner drove to the scene and Sonny rode shotgun. A man with a bloodied head appeared. Nearby, a black Mustang with completely blackened windows was parked. Sonny and his partner went to check if the occupants were witnesses to the fight, or victims.

Suddenly, the Mustang swerved toward another officer, barely missing him. Sonny's partner initiated a pursuit. The Mustang veered into an apartment complex and rammed a police car before heading in the direction of a Native American tribal reservation. A helicopter joined the pursuit and gave directions. Sonny's partner pursued the Mustang onto the reservation and moved into position to do a PIT maneuver to stop the suspect. During the maneuver, the Mustang spun around and locked onto Sonny's vehicle. In full fight or flight mode, Sonny jumped out. He couldn't see the suspect but began yelling commands. As the suspect started rocking the Mustang to free it from the police car, Sonny saw that his partner was caught in his seat belt.

Given that the suspect had already tried to run over one officer and rammed a police car, Sonny realized the suspect had no qualms about harming a law enforcement officer and was about to use the Mustang as a deadly weapon against his partner. Sonny had to make a split-second decision.

He shot six rounds through the driver's side window. The glass shattered and revealed a young man with a shaved head in a beater T-shirt. He was bleeding. Sonny later learned that one of his rounds had passed through his side and missed all his internal organs. The suspect seemed prepared to reach for a weapon. Sonny almost shot again. The PIT maneuver had knocked the Mustang out of gear. The suspect tried to get it back in gear. As the suspect continued to resist, other officers moved into TASE and subdue him. For a moment, Sonny felt relief. He'd stopped the threat and protected his partner.

Then Sonny's eye wandered to the back seat of the Mustang. Someone was sitting there. With horror, he realized the person was dead. He felt his heart rate go through the roof and his blood pressure went off the charts. He called another officer to look in the car. The officer was tall and had to practically double over to see. He looked back at Sonny, his eyes wide and his face white. A young woman lay in the back seat, dead from a gunshot wound. From Sonny's weapon.

Sonny knew instantly that he would never be the same. He had crossed the veil and his life as he knew was over.

He turned and walked off into the desert. "I just wanted to be away from there." He started to cry. His partner found him and gave him some water. The world showed, including reservation police. They drove him back to the station where he was constantly surrounded by people—the chaplain, the police association people, the FBI, peer support.

Initially, he didn't know who the deceased was. A co-worker told him she was a 15-year-old girl, the cousin of the suspect.

In our interview, he said, "That was the worst moment of my life." He looked at me and teared up. "What was her name? I can't remember her name." Finally, he whispered, "Celeste. Her name was Celeste." He had later learned that Celeste and her cousin had been committing crimes together for some time.

Sonny couldn't rationalize killing Celeste. The guilt and shame set in immediately. He loathed himself. "I fucked up. I did a bad job. I expected to be arrested at any time. I was obsessed about what else I could have done." The police association got him out of town as the media attention spiked. He was placed on administrative leave. His department believed in taking care of their people, and he knew they had his back, but he couldn't pull himself together. He believed he didn't deserve support or compassion. The more his department showed support, the angrier he became. He didn't understand the reason he couldn't accept support, or let go of his anger, and the negative judgment he experienced in childhood came back full force, this time self-inflicted.

He sought outside counseling and was diagnosed with PTSD. As time went on, anxiety, sleeplessness, depression, and panic attacks stepped in. He withdrew and lost trust in others, staying in his home for four months doing nothing but playing video games.

The suspect driving the Mustang was charged with two counts of aggravated assault and sentenced to seven years. Although Sonny was cleared in the shooting, his symptoms from the event continued. One of his triggers became the sight of any black Mustang—he startled every time.

When Celeste's mother filed suit against the police department and settled for mid-five figures, Sonny was relieved the case didn't go to trial and was spared having to endure looking at photos of the scene, yet he couldn't shake free of the decision he had made that resulted in Celeste's death.

His attitude had changed, as did his personality. He felt powerlessness over his fate and was too damaged and ashamed to connect with friends and loved ones. Rage became a huge problem. His family noticed. After he lost it in front of his terrified young nieces, they begged their parents not to see him. He ostracized and bullied people. People at work avoided him. He disconnected from his morality and the meaning in his life.

Sonny suffered from a "moral injury." Unlike PTSD, which is based on fear, a moral injury is not a diagnosis—it is based on moral judgment. Sonny's deeply held moral beliefs did not jive with taking a life.

A moral injury is defined as "a particular type of psychological trauma characterized by intense guilt, shame, and spiritual crisis which can develop when one violates his or her moral beliefs, is betrayed, or witnesses trusted individuals committing atrocities" (Jinkerson, 2016). Research shows that the most stressful scenario for a police officer occurs when they seriously injure or kill someone (Violanti &Aron, 1995). Consequences of a moral injury can be increased mental health issues, PTSD, substance abuse, and depression. It can also leave an officer struggling with feelings of rejection, shame, and emotional paralysis, all of which compromise an officer's performance in the line of duty (Papazoglou et al, 2019). Sonny experienced many symptoms of a moral injury, including anger and aggression, an inability to trust, a spiritual crisis, profound sadness, self-hate, and reliving the incident 24/7. He felt like he was losing his soul.

Realizing his nieces were afraid of him got his attention and helped him re-focus on his recovery. Fortunately, he was able to find a spot at the

West Coast Posttrauma Retreat. There, in a safe environment over a six-day period with several other officers who also had sought assistance with lingering trauma symptoms, he began to understand what was happening to him and why his emotions were out of control. He learned coping skills such as anger management. He started to forgive himself for killing Celeste. He began to accept that he was not perfect, but human.

He adopted a tuxedo cat, Baxter. Baxter kept him from isolating by instinctively knowing when to nudge Sonny for petting and when to him alone. Sonny began to sleep better and take care of himself. He wasn't 100%, but he felt so much better that he decided to return to work.

Sonny applied for a position as a gang force detective. He worked four months, then during an evening shift a call came over the radio. "Officer down." An officer had been shot by the passenger in a pick-up truck during a vehicle stop. Unbeknownst to the officer, the suspect had recently committed a murder. Sonny found himself in pursuit of the pick-up truck reaching speeds of up to 130-mph through the mountains in the pouring rain. During the pursuit, the suspect climbed out the rear window and threw items out, impacting and disabling seven vehicles. The pick-up ran out of gas at the top of the mountain. The suspect jumped from the truck and started shooting at Sonny.

A sense of calm came over Sonny as he tried to make his linebacker-sized body small behind the engine block of his vehicle. Then the world began to show up—what seemed like legions of officers. Although he was aware in the confusion that he could die of friendly fire, only later, when he got off operational mode, did the reality set in that he could have died. Slowly, the familiar feeling of vulnerability resurfaced.

After months of feeling safe on the job, he felt knocked down once again by this incident. He first developed claustrophobia, then PTSD symptoms returned this time in the form of anger, crying, and losing control.

He could no longer work the street and accepted alternate duty in the jail. His anger followed him. He ended up hitting a detainee. Finally, a friend took him to a medical practitioner, who prescribed him an antidepressant. The meds helped him control his emotions.

He had loved being a cop, but it was time to let it go. The hard part about retirement was that many of his friends dropped off that map. And the triggers didn't disappear when he quit—even today, years after working through his traumatic events, he still has some.

Ultimately, the high-speed chase on the mountain pushed him into taking responsibility for himself. In order to live, Sonny realized it was time to value his health, and life.

Sonny's healing came from slowly, adjusting to his demons and using his experience to support others who have gone through similar incidents. He had the courage to volunteer with other first responders who were going through hell. He learned he wasn't alone. He kept working on himself in therapy, with EMDR, and in support groups. He finds gratification in helping the community by giving media interviews to educate others. He finds the fact that he can talk about his experiences invaluable both to himself and others. Perhaps most importantly, he took control of his health, lost weight, and has taken on a regular exercise program.

Throughout his hard work to help himself heal Celeste is still on his mind. On the night of Celeste's death, he had only milliseconds to decide how to stop the threat to his partner. The action he took to shoot into the Mustang was instinctual and was motivated to save a life, not take one.

Celeste's shooting changed Sonny forever. Her actual death led to Sonny's figurative death. The taking of a human life under any circumstances can be soul-crushing—even when it is in the process of protecting someone else. Even when it is inadvertent.

Celeste's extended family holds a memorial service for her every year. He has attended twice, most recently in the past year. He thinks about writing to her mother but never has. He continues to feel sad about Celeste's death. He will never completely accept that the shooting was justified, but the image is not constantly in front of his face anymore. It seems more distant—in the past. Another telling moment in his recovery was when he encountered a black Mustang and realized later that he was not triggered.

During our interview, when I asked him what he would have done differently, his eyes focus on the ground. "I would have sought help earlier," he says.

During repair from moral injury, Papazoglou et al. (2019) found that self-care is essential. The path to redemption includes making or seeking amends, engaging in pleasant activities, and communicating with spiritual leaders.

Sonny's attendance at Celeste's memorial services is one method of making amends. Writing to Celeste's mother would be another. His volunteer work helping other wounded first responders certainly counts as penance. Taking responsibility for his health and spending time with his family is pleasurable for him. And his ongoing belief in God has helped immensely.

Sonny delved deeper into his healing hero's journey by examining his life, beginning in his childhood. He began to realize that his upbringing and ordinary world were marked by rejection, abandonment, and judgment, which led to demoralization and self-harm. He recognized that he had been filling the absence of love from his father with junk food. His initial refusal to acknowledge the severity of the problem mirrored his father's refusal to acknowledge responsibility for their unhealthy. Through it all, it reflected a deep-seated belief learned from his father— that he was worthless.

After a time, Sonny had enough of being the "adult" in the relationship with his father. His father had suffered a stroke, so he contacted his stepmother. He told her he loved his father and his second family. He asked to be accepted into their fold. His stepmother immediately became defensive and angry. She was clear that Sonny's request was not in her plans. That was the final contact Sonny had with his father. For his entire life, he had wondered why he wasn't good enough for his father to love him. Suddenly he realized that he wasn't responsible for his father's actions.

He sought more information from other family members and learned that his grandfather was a WWII veteran who suffered from posttraumatic stress disorder. He had been a strict disciplinarian who took his anger out on Sonny's father, who would take the beatings to protect his sisters. Sonny also learned that his father and stepmother were stepsiblings who intermarried. As Sonny understood the degree of dysfunction in his family, he began to let go of his anger and not blame himself anymore for his father's coldness.

Once Sonny realized that his false image of his father, what he wanted to believe of him, was not real, the image shifted. He realized that his father was not the omnipotent man who would rescue, love him, and quell his pain. He realized his father was weak, controlled, and incapable of loyalty. Sonny finally freed himself from the burden of constantly searching for approval and believing his inadequacies were the reason his father abandoned him. It was a small death in a way, a letting go of a false ideal that allowed him to move on.

"It's painful but at least it's not on me anymore," he said with tears in his eyes. "I've been released."

Sonny has found love with a beautiful woman, another first responder who understands him. Together they have settled into a purposeful life. To get to the place where he is now, he seized the sword of knowledge through his hard work on the "inside." Through his struggle with traumatic events, he persevered no matter how he despaired. Over time he learned who he is through hard-won lessons until he experienced the strong positive transformative changes in his perspective. He came to perceive new possibilities for his life's work, his relationships, his appreciation of life, his strengths, and his spiritual life. Each of these points to Posttraumatic Growth.

CHAPTER 6

WILLA

Significant Events
Involving Children

*"Being deeply loved by someone gives you strength while
loving someone deeply gives you courage."*
LAO TZU

Willa's face and presence immediately put you at ease, but if you speak to her for a few minutes, you can sense the toughness underneath. Her face is tan and a bit weathered, but her build is slender and strong. She spends a good amount of time outdoors and could probably beat many men at arm wrestling. If you didn't know she was a 15-year law enforcement veteran, you'd probably pin her as a high school teacher or someone who worked with troubled kids.

She had begun her law enforcement career late after her kids were mostly grown. She was one of the few female officers in her department and the school resource officer. She taught DARE and loved working with teenagers; her background as "mom" made her very good at it. She had "seen it all" when a series of incidents shook her to the core.

Willa graduated from college before women enjoyed equality in the workplace. She began working in retail and soon was promoted to manager, but when she became pregnant, her boss fired her without explanation. Her husband had a good career as a peace officer with good benefits and insurance. She decided to become a stay-at-home parent. She volunteered at her children's school teaching kids how to stay away from drugs, alcohol, and strangers. Once her children were in middle school, she began looking for something to do outside the home. She had always enjoyed working with children. She realized if she became a reserve officer, she would be able to teach the Drug Abuse Resistance Program (D.A.R.E). She joined a large city agency department as a reserve officer and taught D.A.R. E. for five years, then finally decided to attend the police academy.

After she graduated and hit the streets, she decided she wanted to be a real cop and was assigned to patrol. Eventually, she was promoted to field training officer and was responsible for supervising a squad of officers. While she thrived in her job and enjoyed her work, her real love continued to be serving as the school resource officer. During the course of her duties, she worked with kids who struggled with drug and behavioral problems, and worked with staff, kids, and the community over the years to stop aggression and violence at the school. She loved the camaraderie, the action, and feeling like she was making an important contribution to society.

When her husband retired from the city department, Willa decided to retire too, and the family moved to a small California resort town to slow down the pace of life. Willa and her husband bought acreage with room for riding horses and a garden. They figured they would have a relaxed and easy life. They became socially active in church and community activities. Her husband became a reserve officer with a local department. Life was good.

After she settled in, Willa decided she wasn't ready to retire. Her husband's department was short-handed. A position opened at the local law enforcement agency, and she submitted her application. She accepted a reserve patrol, and in less than a year, started working full time as the first and only female in the small department. This was not a problem. She was used to the male world and not intimidated by it. The opportunity to work at the local high school was the cherry on the sundae. She integrated into the community, and everyone she met at the grocery store, church, or school recognized and gave her a friendly greeting. She felt accepted and respected.

The town was quieter than the large city where she'd worked before. Although like most communities, it had its share of drugs, alcohol, and domestic violence, the level of violence was more sporadic and there were days when Willa wouldn't be called for services. While serving in the department, the district attorney initiated a program in which officers were encouraged to arrest offenders, which in turn reduced the number of domestic violence cases. Although the work was rewarding, the department had few officers to cover a wide area, and response times were longer than Willa would have liked. When she worked in the city, she was used to receiving cover within a few minutes; in the rural county, backup was more likely to arrive in 30 minutes or longer. And then there were frequent problems with the communication system and the radio reception.

Nonetheless, Willa enjoyed community policing. She felt accepted and respected. One of her favorite duties was interacting with youth. On school days, she would go to the small high school, meet with the principal, and interact with the students. She was a familiar presence providing security at games and dances, and as she became popular with the kids, they grew to trust her. Among the close connections she developed was Georgia.

Georgia was a "bright star," talented, cheerful, and intelligent. She called Willa "Deputy W" and gave her a big smile whenever they came into contact. Georgia had been dating Gary, who was another of the teens Willa had come to know. She knew Gary and Georgia had verbal arguments; Gary was jealous, possessive, and liked to control Georgia, but Willa never found him to be irrational and never suspected he could become dangerous. Georgia finally broke off her relationship with Gary and began dating Ben. Willa was glad she had found a more suitable young man. On prom night, Willa asked Georgia about Gary. Georgia told her Gary was sad about their breakup and knew she had begun dating Ben but had accepted the situation. She gave no indication that anything was amiss.

Prom night was cool and clear. The teenagers arrived at the gym in sparkling silk and tuxes, corsages, and boutonnieres. A crescent moon softly lit up the hills around the town. The atmosphere was festive. Laughter and dance music filled the air.

After the dance ended, teens spilled out into the streets on their way to make out spots or homes where the parents let them drink beer. Without warning, the cheerful energy was shattered. A woman called the dispatch center screaming hysterically. The dispatcher managed to calm the woman down long enough to get the information: her daughter's boyfriend had been stabbed.

Willa was on patrol and responded to the scene quickly. As she drove down the street a sense of foreboding overtook her. Upon seeing a woman standing on the front steps sobbing, she realized the home was where Georgia and her mother, Marta, lived. She looked down and saw blood on the sidewalk. Marta fell to her knees and sobbed that her daughter and her daughter's boyfriend were dead.

Willa became aware of a horrible sinking feeling in the pit of her stomach. Her heart began racing, but she forced herself to remain professional and keep her own emotions under control. Her first thought was to question Marta, but the woman was too distraught to speak.

Willa took command and managed to lead Marta to safety. Unsure if the scene was secure, she called for backup, but she was the only officer on duty. She was on her own. Her only option was to enter the scene and clear each room as she went. Shaking, she drew her weapon and walked through the front door. She was struck by the pungent stench of cat urine. She cleared the living room and started down the hall to the first bedroom. No one could have prepared her for what she encountered.

Ben was lying on the bedroom floor. His eyes were open, and he seemed to be looking right at Willa. Near Ben, Georgia lay on her stomach. Willa checked her pulse. There was none. As she looked around, she realized with horror that the floor and walls were saturated in blood.

Willa was overcome with a profound sense of helplessness as she continued to clear the rooms. The smell of blood and cat urine comingled. Spontaneously, she held her breath and her heart raced. She felt fear like she never had before. "I'm not prepared for this," she whispered.

After what seemed like an eternity, Willa's training helped her spring into action. She notified dispatch of the homicides and used crime scene tape to secure the scene of the most horrifying crime she'd witnessed in her career. She called dispatch again. An ambulance arrived and attended to Marta, but none of the officers in her department responded. It was a holiday, and no one was on duty. She was alone on scene for forty-five minutes until her husband arrived, followed by the sergeant. All in all, Willa stayed on scene with the bodies of Georgia and Ben for more than six hours. The entire time she was trying to figure out what she could have done to prevent the tragedy.

Willa's gut feeling told her the likely suspect was Gary. He was nowhere in the vicinity of the murders, but Willa later found him at his home. He willingly allowed her to arrest him. He admitted to killing Ben but denied harming Georgia.

While Willa told herself she was fine and coping with the incident well, as time went on, she began to question her perceptions and the reasons she hadn't intervened with Gary before the murders. Although Gary had never appeared irrational to Willa, she knew he was controlling and jealous, the classic signs of an abuser. Later, her confidence was shaken more when she learned that, after Georgia broke up with Gary, he had confronted Ben and verbally terrorized Georgia, and that Gary had sexually assaulted Georgia after he stabbed her.

Willa began interviewing Georgia's friends searching for evidence. She worked overtime for weeks to seek justice for Georgia and Ben to put a damper on the strong emotions she was experiencing. She hoped that exhaustion would keep her from having to feel anger, sadness, grief, and fear. When one of the teens asked Willa how she was coping with the tragedy, she realized how devastated she must have appeared. Six weeks later, her department called for a psychological debriefing. This type of debriefing usually takes place within days after a critical incident.

Although Willa appreciated that she finally had a chance to talk about her reactions to the incident, bringing the subject up after so long a time served to trigger memories that had been partially put away.

Gary's trial for the double homicide with special circumstances began more than a year after the crime. Willa testified in detail about her actions at the scene. Her testimony became a huge trigger, causing her to remember horrific details she had spent months trying to suppress. She was triggered when she watched the news or ran into relatives of Georgia and Ben. The town was small, so she couldn't get away from reminders. She began to have nightmares that she had been shot and no one showed up to help her. She could not tolerate driving by the home where Georgia and Ben were killed. Eventually, she could not bear walking to her patrol car. Her concentration suffered. She became angry with herself for having reactions and told herself to buck up, which only made her feel worse. She didn't understand that she was suffering from classic symptoms of PTSD.

Willa's image of herself as bulletproof was shattered. Her coping mechanisms that had worked for her in her ordinary world were no longer effective. She believed she was a tough cop who could handle anything, yet she began to have nightmares, and her husband began telling her how much the homicides had affected her behavior, ability to cope, and their relationship. She didn't want to see it or hear it, but inside she knew she needed help. Getting it was still out of her reach.

Within months, another teenage boy, Brad, approached Willa. He told her that his girlfriend had broken up with him and he wanted advice on getting her back. Willa knew he was struggling in school and had problems at home. She spent time talking to him and assessed that he seemed rational and was not behaving erratically. Helping teenagers was extremely gratifying to her and she felt good about the interaction.

The next day, she responded to a "shots fired" call. As she drew near to the destination, she heard that there was an attempted suicide. The scene was chaos. Teenagers stood in groups, sobbing, and holding each other. Brad had shot himself in the head while playing Russian roulette. He had been drinking alcohol provided by irresponsible adults; his blood alcohol was almost five times the legal limit. Another deputy on the scene initiated CPR around the time Brad's parents arrived. They were so agitated that Willa responded to them rather than attending to Brad. As she dealt with Brad's distraught parents and friends, she began to have uncontrollable thoughts about the double homicide. Brad died on the way to the hospital. Her sense of failure and self-blame for not predicting Brad's suicide and stopping it was overwhelming.

She went to the high school to provide support for the kids and make sure that they had been offered grief counseling. While talking to them, she became emotional, an unusual reaction for her, and was hit with the realization that she was emotionally traumatized.

As Willa kept working, she gradually noticed the enjoyment she received from her job disappeared. A short time after Brad's suicide, another young man dropped dead from a heart attack. After that, an older man committed suicide. Members of the man's family called her for support. She responded to them but had great personal difficulty watching them try to cope with their loss. She was having a tough time but continued to push her way through her stress symptoms.

The final straw was not another death or community tragedy. It was an attack from within her department.

Impressed by her abilities and experience handling tough situations, her sheriff asked her to apply for a sergeant's position. The community was supportive, but the male deputies were resentful and threatened by an outsider, and a female, outshining them. That's when the betrayal started.

Willa began to sense that the other deputies in her department were overly critical of her. Although she always attempted to get along with them the same way she had with officers in her former department, they seemed to be shunning her subtly and overtly. What she didn't know is that several of the deputies in her department were planning schedule and shift changes without informing her. They held a meeting she couldn't attend and incorrectly told her another meeting had been canceled. She found out in an email that she was scheduled to work graveyard shifts on opposite days that her husband worked.

This schedule change disrupted her interaction with the high school kids, volunteer work, time with her husband, and camping trips with friends. She asked her sergeant for help with the situation to no avail. She filed a grievance, but it was denied. Finally, she attended a meeting with the officers who had changed her schedule without her permission. One told her that the officers had never liked her because she was an outsider. Willa felt hurt and frustrated. Her feelings of betrayal and abandonment translated into an inability to trust those officers while on duty. How could she rely on someone for cover in the field if he had already figuratively stabbed her in the back? She had a nightmare that she responded to a homicide and the officers who betrayed her showed up and laughed at her rather than assisting. She felt isolated and alienated from her department. Finally, her doctor took her off work.

When police officers join a department, they are often told "this is a family." As such, they are led to believe that the department will have their back and protect them from harm. Willa had no reason to think anything else before the homicides. At her previous agency, she felt respected, and she thought there was mutual respect with her coworkers and administration in her new department. However, when her fellow cops became secretive, changed her shift without talking to her, and informed her she wasn't liked because she was an outsider, she was devastated. She lost trust, and the ability to work with people she needed to count on in dangerous situations. Furthermore, when her administration failed to help her, she felt helpless and realized she could do nothing to rectify her situation. Willa's betrayal was both administrative and personal (Kirschman et al, 2014). The personal betrayal occurred when she caught her co-workers in lies and could no longer believe what they told her. The administrative betrayal occurred when she went to her superior officer and asked for help and was essentially abandoned.

Betrayal trauma occurs when people or institutions that a person relies on for protection and survival violate that trust (Freyd, 1994). Whereas recent news stories focus on the betrayal of citizens by law enforcement, the betrayal of police officers by their own departments can set up a situation in which the officer is rendered feeling defenseless and impotent. An officer who can't rely on backup, either from co-workers or the agency is ineffectual. They may become depressed, angry, and even develop posttraumatic stress injury.

In the following weeks, Willa experienced an ordeal of her soul. She became emotionally frozen. She stopped communicating with her loved ones. She stated, "I didn't want to be close to anyone because I didn't want to lose them, so I shut them out, cut them off. I was only hurting them, and myself."

Willa's shock and horror at the murders didn't stop her from maintaining her professional demeanor in face of the most gruesome, heartbreaking scene she had ever witnessed. With support, she might have negotiated her grief and horror, but her unresolved trauma related to the murders was followed by further deaths, then another incident, perhaps even more injurious, when she experienced betrayal and abandonment by her department. Alone and vulnerable, her losses were devastating and left her so demoralized and filled with such self-loathing that her existence seemed pointless. She needed to change or die.

Somewhat impulsively, she decided to get a tattoo of a butterfly to represent her mother who died of breast cancer. The butterfly also signified something larger—Willa's desire to free herself from the emotions that paralyzed her. To do that, she had to look inside herself, in essence become a chrysalis, transform herself, and emerge with new freedom. This was a bold step for her. She was a cop and needed no one, but to end her pain, her attitude would have to change.

Once the psychological "sword" was seized, Willa entered therapy. She began sessions of EMDR, a specific treatment for trauma mentioned earlier. One significant therapeutic insight came when she realized that not allowing herself to feel angry at the senseless waste of lives and at the abandonment and betrayal by her department, she was inhibiting her recovery process. Reluctantly, she accepted the call to make the journey from her ordinary world to the "extra" ordinary inner world. She began to understand that although she was terrified to examine her emotions, reactions, and most private thoughts, she was feeling better.

Willa didn't want to leave her job, but as time went on, she realized she couldn't tolerate any more death or betrayal. She made the choice to leave her department. However, her journey was not over.

Unexpectedly, she found herself in the middle of a lawsuit filed by the family of one of the homicide victims. She states, "I crashed." When school started, she found herself triggered and once again began waking up screaming in the middle of the night with nightmares of the incident. She became angry and felt sad that she was no longer working. She missed her work friends and the kids at the high school. She resented her husband for having a job he liked.

Her path changed again when a parent of one of the murdered children thanked her for being there and taking care of the teenager at the most vulnerable time. Willa understood this was a great gift and she felt loving gratitude. The door to trusting herself opened a crack. She slowly began reaching out for support from her friends and the community. She learned that she wasn't hated by the community as she had been led to believe by some of the other deputies in her department. Maybe there was some good in the world after all.

A spiritual awakening of sorts occurred one stormy day when she was driving at high speed on a stretch of two-lane highway in a remote area in heavy rain. Her vehicle suddenly hydroplaned in a puddle. She immediately and instinctively went into defensive driving mode. As the adrenaline flowed through her veins and her heart pounded, she managed to adeptly slow the car and steer toward safety.

When the car stopped, her hands were shaking. She realized that she had taken an unnecessary risk by driving so fast in hazardous conditions that her reckless actions could have killed her. "To hell with everyone else, I wasn't respecting my own life," she realized. "It hit me like a thunderbolt that I'm not ready to leave this earth."

The temporary loss of control of her vehicle seems like a small incident, but it was remarkably significant in that it jolted her and forced her to face that her carelessness nearly led to her death. As she sat on the side of the road, she realized that to live she had to leave her old expectations behind. She consciously propelled back herself back into life. She began to comprehend that letting go of her career didn't mean the end of her life, but instead could lead to a new beginning and renewed purpose. That realization and her fight to live allowed her to think about continuing her work with the community and fighting breast cancer.

When I asked Willa what the most meaningful part of her journey had been, she answered without hesitation. "Therapy, definitely therapy."

I asked her to explain.

She believes that without the benefit of what she learned in therapy, she would not be out helping children and her community, but hiding in her home isolated, depressed, afraid, and alone. Through therapy, she learned to be aware of her own feelings.

She said, "Therapy was so hard for me. After my session, I would sit in my car outside my therapist's office just trying to process. When I got home, I couldn't talk about it for a day or so because I was trying to absorb all I had learned.

"Once a cop always a cop—we're suspicious by nature. But through therapy, I realized I didn't want to live in a land where I wasn't connected to my loved ones and my community. At that point, I made the choice not to live in the land of paranoia. I had to learn to get to know people before making judgment. Now I look for the better part of people. Because I can understand my own feelings, I'm more aware of other people's feelings. Oddly enough, it's easier to trust people if I understand them."

Her brow wrinkled in thought. "Therapy helped because I was no longer alone. I had a companion who understood and made me feel human. I know so many other cops who didn't reach out, and they are doing poorly."

Tedeschi and Moore (2016) discussed the concept of an "expert companion" as part of the process of posttraumatic growth. An expert companion is not necessarily a professional, but an "expert at providing a sense of compassion and understanding" in the aftermath of traumatic experiences. Expert companions impose no expectations but offer comfort and can stay present throughout the difficult journey to recovery and growth in the aftermath of trauma. They are nonjudgmental and allow the hero to be sad, angry, or depressed without becoming frustrated. They can handle strong emotions and are patient with the challenges and uneven pace of the journey. Expert companions are respectful and have faith in the hero's abilities when providing the hero guidance to keep on the right path. An expert companion listens to thoughts, gives perspective, and helps the hero figure out their belief system. The traumatized person may resist asking for help, but as Willa stated, asking may be the only way to recover and grow.

There are many forms of expert companions. Willa was fortunate to find a therapist she could work with. Other sources may be a trusted friend, an online group or individual, a chaplain, a religious mentor, or God as found in scripture.

Willa has always had a strong faith and has belonged to a tight-knit religious community for her entire life. After the killings and betrayal by her department, she struggled greatly with her beliefs. She stated, "At first, I felt abandoned by God. I thought, 'He's taken away my husband, my family, my community, my self-esteem, and my confidence at my job.' He tested my faith to an extreme. But now I realize that there's a plan in all things, and God put me through this so I could grow in a way I wouldn't have before."

She fought to improve her relationships with her loved ones and to regain her confidence by accepting challenges even when it would have been more comfortable to stay isolated. For example, she accepted the highest position in a local service organization. When people went behind her back to foil her governance, she called them out on their behavior. She said, "I've learned how to acknowledge issues and move on rather than ignore it or stuff it."

"It's all about communication," she says. She has even taught her son, who is also a cop, many of the skills she learned in therapy. And the result? He calls her to talk about incidents that happened to him at work. She has trained him to talk and share his deepest emotions.

"Is there anything else you want to say about your experience?" I ask.

She smiles. "As horrible and deeply painful as my traumas were, I'm a much better person for what I learned about myself. I'm far more aware and connected to the world. I understand people better and have compassion for them when they're not perfect. I can accept that bad things happen and not be angry at God. After all, the world is what it is. I have to admit to that without letting fear overcome me."

"So do you feel cured?" I ask. "Do you still get triggered?"

She looks at me directly. "I can't allow myself to forget what happened. If I put it out of my mind, I won't continue to grow as a person. As long as I'm learning and reaching, I can give 100% of myself. I see that as my growth and my strength."

CHAPTER 7

FRANCINE

Events that are Prolonged and End with a Negative Outcome

"Adversity is like a strong wind. It tears away from us all but the things that cannot be torn, so that we see ourselves as we really are."
ARTHUR GOLDEN

"Find a place inside where there's joy and the joy will burn out the pain."
JOSEPH CAMPBELL

The first thing most people notice about Francine is the way she carries herself—shoulders square, chin up, honest gaze. You half expect her to start telling you how to do whatever it is you're doing better, and she does. The next thing you notice is her sense of humor. She chuckles at the slightest absurdity and follows with a witty remark that perfectly sums up the irony in a situation. She is always alert, the consequence of decades of working as a communications dispatcher and being married to a top cop.

Francine seemed destined to enter a career as a 9-1-1 police and public safety communications dispatcher. She came by it honestly, one might say. Her father served as a news broadcaster in the army and wanted to continue in civilian life. He went to work as a reporter in a small town, a job that required him to work evenings and weekends, and miss special days, the same schedule that first responders encounter. He was the only newsman in the area, so whenever there was a story (fire, bad car accident, etc.), he would get called out, 24/7.

Francine recalls, "My mom didn't like being left alone with us when he got called out in the middle of the night, so they would pack my sister and I up into our station wagon, complete with sleeping bags in the back, and we would go wherever the story was. It was an interesting, and sometimes scary, way to grow up. Interesting because of all the people we got to meet and experiences we got to have. Scary because we didn't always know why we were being dragged out of bed in the middle of the night, and sometimes the scenes we got taken to were not good for kids to be at."

When she was five, her father took the family to a house fire where someone died. Francine vividly remembers the distress of the victim's family looking and waiting for their loved one. She recalls another fire in which lightning hit a tree, knocking it down on a trailer where a grandmother and her grandson were playing a game. The grandmother was killed. These traumatic incidents led to her extreme fear of fire. One day, when she was working fire dispatch, she confessed to a co-worker, who happened to be a firefighter, about the reason she was afraid of fire. He educated her on the science of fire and how it was very predictable. She states, "I will forever be grateful for him doing that."

Francine was exposed to first responder life from the get-go. Not only did she help her father with stories behind the camera, but sometimes she was in front. Her father focused on human interest stories and taught Francine to accept people for whom they were and to communicate clearly, with compassion and confidence. She also learned a sense of responsibility, to pay attention to detail, to maintain grace under pressure, and most importantly, how to multitask. What other kind of career would she have?

There has been some controversy as to whether 9-1-1 police and public safety dispatchers are truly first responders even though they are literally the first to pick up the phone when a call comes in for police, fire, or medical emergencies. From the first second, they are sending out for help through the computer-aided dispatch (CAD) system while at the same time they must remain calm and provide life-saving instructions to civilians, and tactical and emotional support to the responders in the field. They require extensive training and skills including good judgment, the ability to assess situations rapidly, teamwork, memory for codes, places, and details, and complex computer skills. They must keep track of rapidly changing incidents as they cross jurisdictions and require different agencies and disciplines. They are the hub of any crisis.

The Homeland Security act of 2002 (6 U.S.C. 101, section 2) defines first responders as "individuals who, in the early stages of an incident, are responsible for the protection and preservation of life, property, evidence, and the environment." Who better could fit that description but a 9-1-1 dispatcher? (Police 1, 2020)

The stress experienced by 9-1-1 dispatchers is enormous. They hear the calls of people suffering but frequently do not learn the outcome of a call because more calls have come in and they have no time. Research shows that between 17% and 24% of public safety telecommunicators have symptoms of PTSD and 24% have symptoms of depression, yet there is a dearth of research on their suicide risk and mental health. (Tiesman et al, 2021)

Despite their enormous responsibility and exposure to critical incidents, they have been classified as administrative support, resulting in inadequate pay, working conditions, training, and access to benefits. A call to change the Standard Occupational Classification of 9-1-1 dispatchers to "protective" has largely failed, but some states and agencies have passed resolutions or bills to classify public safety dispatchers as first responders.

Francine decided to be a communications dispatcher after she married her first husband, a law enforcement officer. When he and the other cops got together, they complained the dispatchers and how they didn't always do or get the officers what they needed when they needed it. When Francine realized those people—dispatchers—had her husband's life in their hands, she decided to enter the field so she could make sure her husband and friends were kept safe. Back then there was no academy to go to—it was more like on-the-job training. She started in the Los Angeles Dispatch Center for the CHP, working the graveyard shift with her husband, and discovered she loved it. She took to the adrenaline rush like a duck to water.

Graveyard shift in a large LA dispatch center was busier than swing shift in most areas, and there was always something going on. Her coworkers worked as a team to track calls and anticipate what the officers would need. Occasionally, when the officers weren't talking on the radio and the phones weren't ringing, they would sit with their feet up.

Francine recalls, "One of those nights a strange voice came on my radio saying, 'Hello? Is anyone there? I see a patrol car here, but I don't see your officers.' The gentleman on the radio was a tow truck driver who saw the lights on the patrol car and stopped because he didn't see anyone around it." Back in those days, the units didn't call their location in when they made a traffic stop, so she had no idea who or where they were. She initiated a roll call to see who it might be. When the officers arrived, they found the other officers lying outside their vehicle. They'd both been struck by a drunk driver. One had been thrown into the center divider by the impact, the other had been thrown down an embankment.

"That was the night I realized I never wanted to hear anyone's voice on the radio other than my officers because that meant something bad had happened to them. It was my first officer-involved incident where one of my guys got hurt, but not the last. I have had officers get shot at, get shot, run over, get in accidents, and I once worked a law enforcement helicopter crash. Every one of those incidents took a bit out of me."

In the large LA dispatch center, the dispatchers knew the names of the officers, but never saw them. The officers worked out of a separate building, and only came in for training or to show trainees the dispatch center. When Francine left LA and started working in smaller dispatch centers, she finally got to put faces to the names on the roster. Whereas she had always done her best, putting a face to the voice asking for backup or an ambulance made a difference, and her job became more personal.

She recalls, "I had a cop friend who worked motors in LA. I happened to be working the radio when he got run over. I did everything in my power to make sure he was taken care of. We both transferred out of that area to other offices and then ended up together again. I was working the radio when he got into his second accident on his motor. It was the end of my shift, but I wouldn't leave the radio until I knew he was all right. I went to visit him one day after his accident and said that I was never going to work his radio again because I felt like I jinxed him. He told me that he wanted me on there if something happened to him because he knew I'd do everything in my power to make sure he got what he needed. Unfortunately, he did have a third accident, and I worked that one, also. The third was sadly the end of his career. We remained good friends for a long time after he retired, and he even introduced me to my second husband."

She stayed with that agency for seven years, working in four different offices. She transferred to a local Sheriff's Office for the rest of her career. Her former department was busy, but it had nothing on the more rural SO. Her center dispatched law, fire, and EMS. She recalls, "I was amazed at all the violence that took place in my county. Sometimes everyone was maxed out and there was no way to keep up with all the calls for service that came in. It's a very helpless feeling, when calls keep coming and you have absolutely no one to send."

Although Francine never left the dispatch center without knowing the status of her officers, that wasn't the case with citizen calls. Dispatchers often don't know the outcome of the calls that they generate. "Once I was on the phone with a woman who had a prowler in her house. I stayed with her, telling her where to hide, asking where the intruder was, and keeping her calm when he entered the room, she was in. We bonded in those few minutes, both knowing that if I couldn't get the officers there that she may not make it. As soon as the officers got there she hung up, and that was that. I had to handle many other calls and had forgotten about the women until I went home. Then I wondered who the intruder was—

did she know him? Was he there to rob her? Was it a joke? I'll never know. Dispatchers have no closure for most of the calls. It can be frustrating, stressful, and upsetting, but that's the nature of the job."

Then there are "repeat" callers. Francine recalls one woman who called almost every Friday night because she had been assaulted and injured by her boyfriend after he went out drinking with his buddies. She ended up in the hospital several times, and badly beaten and bruised. Francine spent months encouraging her to get her strong enough to leave the boyfriend and go to a safe house, or at least have a safety plan. She did leave him once but went right back.

Francine says, "Domestic violence is really like an illness to some of the victims. They have nowhere else to go, and at least they know the person they're with versus being thrust out into the world alone. Unfortunately, I remember the Friday night I got the call to her apartment, and the officers found her dead. To this day, I remember the boyfriend's name but still can't remember hers."

Dispatcher centers are the hub of activity in disasters. Francine's county borders a river and is prone to flooding. In 1986, one of the biggest floods occurred blocking all ingress and egress routes. People had to be rescued from their flooded homes. The dispatchers worked to make sure the deputies received the allied agency support including Chinook helicopters from the National Guard to help with rescues. Deputies patrolled deluged streets in boats to try to get to the residents who couldn't evacuate in time.

Francine recalls, "One elderly woman called in, and she was really scared. She wanted to leave but her husband wouldn't go, so she felt stuck. I told her she needed to make up her mind before dark because they couldn't do rescues after dark. Later that night, I got her on the phone again and she was hysterical. Water was coming into their house, and she didn't know what to do. I knew that the water was rising and that it was going to get worse before it got better, and I had serious concerns about the couple's safety. However, I couldn't put my guys at risk by trying a nighttime rescue. I have no idea whatever happened to her and her husband, but I have always felt bad that she was in danger."

Francine explains, "The job is constant stress, a constant adrenaline rush, constant multi-tasking—yet all quite addictive. There is nowhere to go when everything's happening. During major incidents, we barely have time to go to the bathroom (and in fact often can't leave the radio that long) or to eat. Nonetheless, I truly loved that job but didn't know the price I was paying mentally for doing it."

The price includes being treated poorly by coworkers she tried to protect. "Some cops seem to think dispatchers are 'lesser' people, just there to do the officers' bidding. They order, rather than ask, and complain if they don't get what they want as soon as they want it. Field personnel may not realize that dispatchers are responsible for everyone who is working. While one unit in a quiet sector is upset because they didn't get the tow truck they ordered quickly, another unit on the other side of the county is dealing with a stolen vehicle with an armed suspect. The same dispatcher is working both calls. It can be tricky."

She recalls another flood when she went in early to acclimate before her shift started. "I plugged into the main law radio with the day shift dispatcher. However, as soon as I did, she unplugged and left, leaving me with a total mess. I had no idea where anyone was or what resources had been called. Even worse, I had no idea what had been asked for but not received yet. It was a terribly helpless feeling.

"Just then, of the admin guys came over to me and stuck his head over my radio. At the time, I was dealing with some radio traffic and trying to figure out what was happening. He loudly demanded to know where a certain unit was. I told him I had no idea. He then proceeded to loudly say how incompetent I was, and I shouldn't be doing the job if I couldn't keep up with the work. It was one of the few times I really felt like crying at work—but I couldn't. I had a job to do despite him, and I did it."

Fortunately, most officers understand and appreciate dispatchers. In Francine's agency, when deputies are injured, they are often assigned to dispatch if they can't perform their regular duties. Almost every single one leaves dispatch with a totally new respect for what dispatchers do, are educated, and become easier to work with once they got back on the street.

The incident that changed Francine's life started out on a normal day and ended up changing her worldview. It was a critical incident that seemed to go on forever and ended in tragedy. Francine's natural confidence was put to the test during the incident that caught the nation's attention.

Francine recalls, "I was working swing shift, 3:00 p.m. to 11:00 p.m., at the sheriff's office on a Friday. I received a call from our dispatch center telling me there had been multiple homicides, so to expect a busy shift. I decided to bring my dinner to work because there probably wouldn't be any breaks to go out. Like most of my workmates, I went into work early to help.

"When I officially started my shift at 3:00 p.m., we knew that there were five homicides and one attempted homicide in three different locations. The suspect had already killed his wife, sister-in-law, mother-in-law, and a coworker, and attempted to kill another coworker. His three small children were missing. A manhunt was on to find the kids, the assumption being that their father had taken them. A BOLO (be on the lookout) had been put out on the vehicle and the suspect.

"Everyone on our shift was immersed in the 'normal' organized chaos that accompanies all major incidents. Because of the type of crime and the different crime scene locations, all the on-duty deputies were tied up and we were only dispatching in-progress emergency calls. All other callers were either told that someone would be out the next day to talk with them, or they could go into the offices to make a report. Most people were understanding about this, some were not.

"At the beginning of my shift, I was working the main law radio. Normally, this position wouldn't answer phones, but due to the BOLO, the phones were ringing off the hook with suspect sightings, all of which needed to be logged and broadcast on the radio. Due to the number of calls coming in, and the fact that all the units were busy, the suspect 'sightings' were dispatched in the blind (meaning they were broadcast on the radio as information), time-stamped, and filed away. We thought the suspect was most likely out of the county by that time, possibly headed to Mexico, so we didn't worry too much about all the suspect sightings. As the long day progressed, the children were still not found.

"Around four, the radio was quiet for a moment, so I answered one of the 9-1-1 calls. A woman was on the line saying she knew the suspect and knew his car. She had just seen him by the county dump pushing the kids down on the floorboard of his car. I made an incident card, thanked her, broadcast it in the blind, stamped and filed it away, and didn't think any more of it.

"The entire shift that night was very intense. We had received information confirming that the suspect was indeed heading south, and we started working with the FBI to coordinate information. At one point, I was walking to the Lieutenant's office to relay some info from the FBI, and I walked by the ID Bureau, what is now called CSU.

"Back in those days, the ID office was on one side of a hallway, and the lab was on the other. It was always fascinating to walk by the lab because they often had interesting evidence laying around or hanging up. I walked by the lab and remembered seeing a slip dress in an unusual, beautiful shade of pink. I continued past the lab and delivered my message to the lieutenant. On the way back, I thought I'd check that dress again. When I got to the lab, I saw the dress—and noticed a white swath on the bottom, which was the original color. It was then I realized it was the blood-soaked slip from one of the victims who had been killed. I can still see that slip clearly in my mind to this day.

"As the evening wore on and the suspect got further away from our county, dispatch calmed down a bit and we all were able to get off work at our regular time. I remember thinking about the kids and hoping they were safe, wherever they were.

"The next day was a Saturday. My husband, who was a deputy, had a meeting across town and left the house early. Around 9:00 a.m., dispatch called. They found the children. Two were murdered, their throats slit, and their bodies thrown into a ditch. The third, the five-year-old, was alive with a slit throat. The office was notifying everyone who had worked on it before we could hear it on the news.

"I asked where they found the kids. They said they were found in the dump. My mind went to the phone call from the woman who said she knew the suspect and saw him in his car by the dump.

"I immediately took on the guilt of those kids dying, and the one having to stay in the dump all night with a slit throat and two dead siblings. I remember it strongly affected me, and I felt totally lost.

"It was my day off but needed to be in dispatch with 'my people.' I decided to take in some cookies. When I walked in the atmosphere was heavy—we had all been working hard to get those kids back, and the reality of the outcome was numbing. I felt like a zombie, and that's all I remember until I met my husband and for lunch. I remember feeling spacy.

"My husband asked me what was wrong, and I told him about the kids, and I cried—right there at the table with our friends. He tried to calm me down, but I do remember somewhere in the conversation he said it might be time for me to look for another job because it was taking too much out of me.

"The autopsy determined that the children had been killed the previous morning. They were dead long before I received the call about the dump."

Embedded in Francine's mind was the irrational "magical" thought that if she'd been better at her job all three children would have been saved. The subsequent guilt and shame nearly destroyed her life. She spiraled into depression and isolation.

She discussed the emotional and psychological cost of a child's death, and how the resultant destructive self-talk eventually ended her career. Most first responders agree that calls involving children are the worst, the ones that embed deepest in the mind, and are the most likely to bring up painful emotions. If the job of a first responder is to protect the vulnerable, children are the most in need. When talking to a first responder about the death of a child, you are likely to hear them described as innocent and blameless. A first responder can mitigate the impact of the death of an adult, e.g., "He lived a long life," "She was partly to blame," but there is no way to diminish the death of a child.

After the critical incident, she started having issues with stress at work. On one hand, she wondered if she was reacting to the negative environment that can arise in dispatch centers. On the other hand, she loved her job and didn't want to leave. She decided to tough it out. She tried to manage her stress by quitting full-time and working per diem so she could choose who she worked with and get away from some of the "toxic people in that tiny, airless room." It seemed to help, and she kept dispatching for a few years, but continued to experience stress symptoms—depression, isolation, anger, and exhaustion.

She says, "Don't get me wrong, dispatch wasn't all stress and constant work. There were often quiet times, or quiet radios. Most of my co-workers were great to work with, and we had a lot of fun. To deal with our jobs, we were all very, very good at gallows humor. A lot of what was said was totally inappropriate and would never be said outside of dispatch. Yet, it was what kept us sane. But no one outside of our little room knew the pressures and stressors that we experienced, even the cops, firefighters, and medics we work with."

Francine's final straw occurred in 1992. She took a call in the early afternoon from a woman who was worried about her mother who had recently left an extremely abusive relationship with her dad and moved in with the daughter in Berkeley. The mom had returned to Sonoma County to take a Christmas present to her son who was still living with the dad. Mom hadn't called the daughter or come back to Berkeley, and the daughter was concerned and wanted a welfare check. Francine took the information and dispatched a deputy to the house. There was no response to a knock on the door, so they cleared the scene with no contact.

Francine continues, "Shortly before 5:00 p.m. that day, we were going to swing shift. Most of the deputies were in the office either getting off work or coming on to their shift. I was working phones when the same woman called.

"When I heard her voice, my intuition kicked in and I just knew it wasn't going to be good. I called the substation where the call was to be dispatched to and talked to one of the oncoming deputies. He knew me and didn't take my 'spidey' sense lightly, so when I told him he needed to make entry into the house, he listened.

"The dad was there this time, and they made entry—and found the mom dead in the bathtub. Their son was there, and another deputy came to get him to take him to juvenile hall to await his sister coming to get him. The boy didn't look too distraught, so the deputy took him to McDonald's to get something to eat and interview him a bit. She asked if he saw what happened.

"The boy replied, 'Yeah, Dad hit Mom with a baseball bat. But she deserved it.'

"This deeply affected the deputy who was transporting him. She came into dispatch after she dropped him off and told us what he had said and how he had said it—so matter-of-factly.

"It affected me to the core. That was my last shift in dispatch. I just couldn't deal anymore with the violence that people perpetrate on each other—especially on the innocent ones."

After leaving dispatch, Francine tried to figure out what to do with her life. "I'd love to say that life improved as soon as I left the job, and all was well—but that would be a lie. I never dealt with the stress, and my symptoms kept getting worse. I don't think I was a very nice person to be around for a while."

Her husband, a deputy, supported her leaving the job, but unfortunately dispatching was in her blood. Her husband still got do his job. She would sit home, depressed at not knowing what was 'really' going on. She would thirstily ask her husband what happened at work every day when he came home. She describes the feeling. "For years, whenever I heard a siren, I had an almost visceral pull to go to wherever it was and see what was going on. It was incredibly hard not to. Anytime I felt stressed about life, the thought would go through my mind, 'Just go back to dispatch. Everything will be better if you just go back.' The job was like an addiction, and I was hopelessly hooked with no relief in sight."

Finally, a friend told her about the West Coast Posttrauma Retreat (WCPR). She asked what she had to do to qualify for WCPR. Her friend said, "Oh, don't worry. You qualify."

Francine describes her experience. "The first thing I learned at WCPR was that there was something going on with me (I had PTSD), and the second thing was that there was help. It took me thirteen years after my main incident to seek help, so it was a lifesaver to be with a group of people who really understood what I had been through and how to recover from it. Fortunately, my recovery from PTSD, while not quick, has been a steady road of getting my life back.

While at WCPR, she learned about 'adrenaline addiction' that explained the physiological responses she experienced when hearing sirens or a police radio/scanner. She notes, "It is so hard to explain to anyone who hasn't experienced it, and it was hard to explain to myself. I hid a lot of my feelings from my husband so he wouldn't think I was nuts. I isolated from any friends I had and gotten depressed."

She also learned about suicidal ideation. Although she wasn't actively suicidal, there were times when she felt it would be fine if she didn't wake up in the morning. She discovered that others felt the same. She recalled, "One night when I was still working in dispatch, we told each other how we would commit suicide. We had all worked enough suicides, and we didn't want our loved ones to suffer the way the folks we dealt with, the survivors, suffered. I remember some creative methods that were described that night. We were all joking around, but now looking back on it I wonder . . ."

As Francine developed self-knowledge and skills, she came to realize that she was the adult child of an alcoholic mother. One day, her mother didn't answer the phone. Concerned, Francine and her husband went to her house, but no one let them in. They broke in and found her mother drunk on the floor with an injured hand. They tried to wake her, but her mother played possum until they tried to take her to the emergency room. Then she became remarkably resistant.

After they got her to the hospital, her blood alcohol was measured at 2.0, two and one-half times the legal limit. A social worker was blunt, "You know she's an alcoholic and has been for years." It dawned on Francine that she learned many co-dependent behaviors to negotiate her mother's drinking and to survive her childhood.

Francine became infuriated. Suddenly, it all made sense. She later learned that several people had been suspicious about her mother's drinking all along, but no one had said anything.

She joined Al-Anon and began to connect the dots. Her mother had never treated her well. As a kid, Francine couldn't talk to her mom until she'd had her first glass of wine. When Francine's father died, her mother became demanding and dependent. Nothing was ever good enough. She took credit for all the good things Francine did and blamed her when things went wrong. She was spiteful—she sold the only thing Francine wanted from her grandfather—a rocking chair he had made.

Francine learned how her harsh self-judgment, which is universal in responders who expect to control all aspects of a critical incident, can bring a career to the verge of ruination. She became a "responsibility absorber" probably by modeling her father and feeling duty-bound to take care of her helpless mother. Whatever the situation, she would take it on, even at her own peril. She could never say "no" because if she didn't do it, who would? She told herself the world would fall apart if she wasn't in the thick of it. This attitude might have made her good at her job, but it also negatively impacted her health and well-being.

Healing comes from confronting the myth that perfection is possible during chaos and giving up the fallacy that a less-than-perfect outcome means incompetence. Francine had to face hard truths about herself. She couldn't do everything. She was human and vulnerable. Another huge part of her journey has been to allow others to make mistakes. She states, "The biggest thing is to let life happen and relinquish control." She's still working on avoiding negativity, a common foible of first responders.

Francine says, "I think one of the biggest, yet least recognized, parts of PTSD is that it robs you of your belief in a higher power." She once asked a co-worker one time if they believed in God, and their response was, "No, because if there was a God, then why did he let that old lady fall on the floor and lie there for so long that her cats ate her?"

A lot of first responders have plenty of "if there was a God, then why . . ." stories. Yet, for Francine, her real healing started when she opened to spirituality. She didn't trust churches, but I knew that she needed something. Fortunately, she had friends who like to study and learn about different spiritual beliefs. Some of these beliefs felt like coming home, and she started her own spiritual journey. "For me, having faith in something bigger than me takes the burden off my 'I must do everything' personality type. I have learned to sit back for a bit and take a breath before reacting (okay, I don't do this all the time, but I'm working on it). I have learned that it's not all up to me to fix everything. I have learned that sometimes stuff just happens—there isn't anything I can or could have done to make it any better. I have learned to let people have their own experiences without me having to try to make things 'perfect.' And I have learned that 'perfect' isn't sustainable or even attainable, to a large extent. I don't have all this mastered yet and I sometimes have setbacks, but I think that's part of being a normal human being."

Her relationships have gotten better and better as time has gone on. "Post-PTSD, I have worked to find out who I am. I am the daughter of an alcoholic, and I learned that I am really good at being co-dependent. I have worked long and hard to recognize when I may be doing things that aren't in my best interest, or that are meddling where I don't belong. I became a 'fixer' in my family when I was quite young and that is a hard, hard habit to break, though I'm doing a good job these days in letting things just happen without having to fix them. I have recognized that being co-dependent was part of why I was such a good dispatcher—give me a problem, and it's in my DNA to fix it. I also recognize that a lot of co-dependent behaviors aren't healthy or good for me, so I'm working on gently teaching myself to do things differently. I can't say the road had been easy because it's been rocky and hard at times. However, I wouldn't change things for the world."

Part of her spiritual journey has been learning to have gratitude for everything that happens in life. She believes there is always at least one thing to be grateful for. Although she would have preferred not having some of her negative experiences, they have brought her to where she is today. "I'm surrounded by people who really care about me—not what I can do for them or what they can get from me, but ME. Gratitude is my premier spiritual practice, and I practice it every day. I'm grateful to have had a job that I loved with all my heart. I'm grateful that I found someplace that could help me deal with PTSD and get my life back. I'm grateful that I'm still connected with so many of the people that have helped me along the way. I'm grateful that I'm alive right now and have the relationships I have. Without the bad times, I wouldn't be aware of the good times, and I'm truly grateful for the good. Life goes on after PTSD."

Through her self-searching, Francine reassessed her value to the world, grew spiritually, and turned her trauma into a gift. Ultimately, she "returned with the elixir," the magic potion that she could offer to others and allow her to continue her journey. She became a chaplain and involved herself in helping other first responders at WCPR. One of the skills she teaches is gratitude, the quality of being thankful and appreciative.

The death of the children and many of the other calls Francine took were truly horrible and she will never forget, but without those experiences, she might not have never found the way to her spiritual connections or to advance her ability to help others on a deeper level. She was able to alter what she expected her life to be and instead identified in herself what was needed to facilitate growth and then take those lessons to help transform others' lives. It's called posttraumatic growth.

CHAPTER 8

DILLON, PART 2

Personally Threatening Situations

"Bring the past only if you're going to build from it."
DOMENICO ESTRADA

"Something dead every day."

Dillon and I were talking about the day of the multiple car accident. He asked, "Do you want me to tell you about the day Rich died?"

I nodded.

He leaned forward in his chair. "Three of us CHP patrol guys started working at four in the morning. It was winter and the weather turned nasty—wet and cold and the sky was dumping rain and hail like end times. We got a call about a crash south of town. My partner was sent up north to chain control 'cuz it was snowing up there. I went south. On the way, I hear the dispatcher putting out a couple more crashes. I see one on the north side of the road, but I decide the south side seems busy, so I keep rolling. I see black pavement—maybe a little wet, but not raining. I'm going about 80 and all of a sudden, right at the top of the hill, the road turns white. It was weird 'cuz it doesn't snow there, and the road went from black to white like a line on the pavement. The road was really slippery, and the car got a little loose, so I let off the gas. Then the road is black again. I see taillights a quarter mile in front of me and then I didn't see them again. It was weird. The road is white again and I'm slowing down. I didn't realize at the time it was hail. I get to the exit just past the bridge, and there's a gold Lexus upside down over the embankment. I stop and the driver is getting out of the Lexus. He's fine. I go down and ask him if he's okay. He says he's the only one, and he'll call his son who's a deputy to come get him. I call for a tow truck and the son shows up to get the driver, so I start back up the embankment.

"I'm walking up the hill and I hear this strange sound. I look and there's this Cadillac coming across the freeway, sideways, right at me. It looked like it was going to hit my patrol car, so I run. The Cadillac passes my car and jumps over the embankment and slides off. He landed literally right on top of the other crashed car. I put that out as an 1183—an accident with no details. The driver gets out pretty quick and asks me if I'm okay because he thought he'd hit me. I'm a little shaky, but I say I'm okay and he says he's okay, too.

"The tow truck arrives for the first car, and I advise that we're not towing anyone until the weather clears because it's just too dangerous. In the meantime, I call the talk show guys I know at a local radio station and tell them to broadcast that we have hail in the area and to slow down. So, I feel like I was doing everything I can.

"Then, the fire department is responding. I see them running northbound Code 3 with their lights and sirens on, and I know they're going to go over the off-ramp and come back. I call dispatch and advise that the crash is non-injury and to cancel fire and the ambulance, but then they're right there parking in front of my vehicle. It's Rich, and we walk down the embankment to the cars.

"Rich talks to the drivers and asks them if they need help. They say no, and he gets them to sign a medical release.

"The last thing I say to Rich is 'Let's get out of here. There's no sense in standing around for one of us to get killed.' So, we walk back up the embankment again.

"Just as I crest the top of the freeway—I didn't hear it—but I saw car number three—a pickup truck—coming sideways the same way as the Cadillac sliding right at us. I don't remember what I yelled—look out or fuck or something—but at the same time, I was running. I didn't have as much time this time, so I physically had to dive like superman over the embankment. It was dark. I landed on the rocks and rolled down the hill. At one point as I'm rolling down the hill, I was sliding backwards on my back, and I could see the truck going over nose-down tail-up, and I see two people disappear. I must have injured my leg 'cuz it hurt like hell. I put out to dispatch that there are all kinds of wrecks, get all units rolling. There was so much radio traffic that the dispatcher didn't hear me, so I said, '11-99. Officer down.' Meaning I was down. That silenced the traffic and I said what happened.

"I'm hurting so bad, and the truck was so close, I think I've been hit. But I say I'm okay. I'm down at the bottom of the embankment, and I crawl maybe ten feet to get behind an oak tree in case another car comes down. My partner is suddenly there yelling, grabbing me, making sure I'm all right. I see a young fire volunteer running around screaming, 'Captain Rich. Captain Rich.' It was almost like a cartoon, but then I realize he's already in shock. My partner goes over to the truck and calls in that he has one unconscious and needs an ambulance. It was the driver of the Cadillac—he hadn't made it up the embankment and got hit by the truck.

"My partner looks around and says he can't find Rich. It seemed like an eternity. Finally, I hear him say in my earpiece that there's an 1181—a minor injury—and one probably 1144 firefighter. He was dead. Rich was dead.

"I must have gone into shock. The sun is coming up and there are all these helicopters flying around, and there's all these lights on the road and people everywhere doing CPR on Rich, and they're back boarding me and pulling me up the hill. They roll me to the hospital helicopter and start putting me in. Suddenly, they start arguing about which helicopter they're gonna transport me in. The sergeant says, 'No you're fucking not taking him in that helicopter. He's a Chippy and he's going in the goddam CHP helicopter. Take him to the CHP helicopter.' So, they roll me over and unload me again into the CHP helicopter."

Dillon spontaneously laughed. "And on top of all this, my mind flashes that when I was hiding behind the tree, my cell rings. I answer, and it's my daughter wanting to know if I was going to pick her up to take her to school for cheerleading practice. I say, 'I just got hit by a car, but I'm okay.' She says, 'Oh. Okay. Thanks.' And hangs up like 'fuck, he's not gonna take me to school.' Later, my wife said she woke up to my daughter saying, 'Dad was hit by a car and can't take me to school, so can you take me?'

"I get to the hospital and get wheeled in. They're real careful to take off my jumpsuit because it's a $350 suit. They start checking my leg. I'm in a room across from Rich's body. All I can hear is people wailing and sobbing and his wife crying. People are showing up from my office telling me 'Thank God,' they're glad I'm alive.

"In hindsight, that's when my survivor's guilt started. It got me for a long, long time during lots of alcohol and many rehabs. I wished I'd gotten hurt worse so I'd feel more justified, like maybe more of a near-death experience would justify my life.

"When I went to Rich's funeral I was on crutches. Right before it started, I was at the door, and the auditorium was packed, and people were standing outside. I'm in my uniform and my captain was there and they put me in front next to Rich's wife and kids. I'm right up front and it was so sad to see the flag presentation. I hoped I'd seen my last at Lee's funeral.

"So, it's over and I'm leaving and the captain's like, 'Hey Dillon. I want to introduce you to . . .' And, he says my name and he's introducing me to Senators and Congress people, and he says, 'This is the hero who was at the crash . . .'

"And I heard the word 'hero' and I died inside. I told my wife I have to get out of here. I have to leave, get away from here. I got out as quickly as I could.

"After that, things went into a blur. My drinking got really bad . . . really, really bad. I drank morning, noon, and night. My leg healed, but I'd start drinking as soon as I woke up. I'd drink vodka and put it in water bottles so no one would know. I didn't understand what was happening to me, but I did know I wanted to die, and that suicide was a viable option. My wife got all the guns out of the house, but I still had my service weapon. And I can tell you exactly what the steel of the barrel of my gun tastes like because there were times when I put it in my mouth. I didn't want to fuck it up, so I thought about using two guns at the same time.

"I was so tired of letting my wife and family down. Sometimes, I'd disappear and hide out on our patio boat at the lake. I'd take alcohol and no food and stay there for days.

"Guys at work tried to help me. I told them I'm an alcoholic and was protected by the ADA. I was diagnosed with alcoholism and PTSD—dual diagnoses. I'd go to rehab, get out, and start drinking again. My wife was done. She started selling my stuff and making her exit plan."

Finally, Dillon stopped drinking, at least long enough to go back to work for a few weeks. He was keeping his shit together until he had another trigger that took him right back to Sergeant Lee.

He got to the office before daybreak. During the morning briefing, Officer Cain walked in. Officer Cain was an officer Dillon didn't know well. The room went suddenly silent. Hush-hush. The hairs on the back of Dillon's neck stand up. "I'm thinking, 'WTF.'"

"After the briefing, on my way to the locker room, I say to one of my friends, 'Cain reminds me of Lee.'

"Then I walk into the locker room and Cain is standing right there. I didn't expect it. He has this crazy look on his face. I try to act casual and say, 'How ya doing.' He doesn't acknowledge me. He just looks right through me, and I think, 'Whoa. I know this guy, and he's always happy and joking and now he just looks awful.' I'm thinking Cain overheard what I said about Lee and is angry with me. His gun is hanging in his locker, and he puts his hand on it. My heart starts pounding—my mouth goes dry. I get an image of being back in the vehicle bay looking at Lee's body. My body is reacting like 'run.'

"I back out of the locker room, and I walk into the sergeant's office to see if something is going on with Cain. I ask, 'Is there an officer safety issue about Cain?'

"The sergeant says, 'I don't know. Why?'

"And I go, 'He's acting weird.'

"The sergeant goes, 'Well, he just had a Form 8.'"

Dillon learns that Cain was under investigation for having sexual contact under the color of authority with a woman he'd arrested. Lee had been accused of the same charges right before he committed suicide.

"First, I was scared for me. Cain could have fucking killed me right there in the locker room, and then I was like, he's gonna eat his gun 'cuz nobody . . . Lee had a Form 8, and nobody talked to him. He didn't have counseling, and he still had his gun, and he killed himself. And Cain had a Form 8 and he looked distraught, and he still had his gun, and nobody was talking to him, and he was all by himself in a locker room."

So, I snap. I tell the sergeant, 'You didn't take Cain's fucking gun. He could have killed me in there. He's got his hand on his gun, and he's bird-dogging me.'

"Suddenly, everyone starts scurrying and things get crazy, and people are running all around. I'm fully dressed in my uniform ready to go to work. And I lose it. I'm crying like a baby, and I can't stop. I get in my car and drive off. I just leave."

At the point in our interview, Dillon was visibly agitated. He looked shaky and sweaty. His sympathetic nervous was clearly activated. He continues as if the incident happened yesterday. I could tell that he still felt threatened by Cain. He perceived that Cain was a true threat.

"Did you flash on Lee?" I asked.

"Yeah, it was totally a Lee flashback. It was the stripes on Cain's pants. Lee's pants had stripes just like that.

"I don't think I made it home before I started drinking again. I was angry. I just lost my shit. I had every emotion you can have. I didn't know what else to do but drink. I'm off work again, burning vacation and 4800 time. I'm a mess, and my head's never really been on straight."

In *The Emotional Brain: The Mysterious Underpinnings of Emotional Response* (1996), author Le Doux notes, "The (traumatized) brain enters into a vicious cycle of emotional and cognitive excitement and, like a runaway train, just keeps picking up speed." Dillon's brain was a runaway train. He was beginning to believe everyone, and everything was a threat. He couldn't stop the thoughts and visions no matter what he did. The drinking helped quell his anxiety—for a while until it didn't. And he couldn't seem to stay sober no matter how hard he wanted to.

"So, after a year of disability, my captain talks to me and suggests I go out on disability retirement. I tell him I'm not old enough. I love this job. He says if I put in my paperwork, I can go out honorably and have a right to reinstatement. He makes me feel better about it and I file the papers.

"I got the letter that I'd been approved in the mail. I opened it and a weight lifted off me. Yes, I loved that job, but really if you look at it, what I loved was being in uniform, driving around in a patrol car, and helping people. It's not running from cars that are trying to kill you, or people who spit on you, or doing reports, or fighting suspects, it was the image I was in love with.

"I loved helping people, but as more time went by, the further the department was behind me, my life just kept improving and improving. I went back to WCPR as a peer, and it was good for me to be in a safe place and help people in a different way.

"I feel really good about myself, not in a cocky or arrogant way, but I feel good in the fact that I can still see a CHP car and have that moment where I wish I was dressed up and driving that car and then I sit with it for a moment and realize I'm in a much better place. I understand that everything is behind me now for a reason and that to go backwards, for anything, would be a detriment to the happiness I have today.

"Some of those instances haven't left me, but I can't see them minute by minute anymore or see them when I'm watching a movie or looking at a wall. I guess everything I've done to get to this point has—I don't want to jinx it by saying healed—but has put me in a good spot. I can feel grateful and thankful for the things I have and where I am in life."

I asked him how he thinks he's changed.

"I think the cop thing was my identity. For a long time, it was all I knew. I was afraid of losing myself and over time I learned more about myself and that I wasn't just Officer Dillon and that I could help people without a uniform on and I could still get some of the satisfaction from not driving a patrol car and going to help someone else.

"Once I could get over it, once I learned there's life after the highway patrol. I found things that could make me happy outside the department. It was a gift to find out I had more than one Dillon in me.

"Now I think learning to look outside my comfort zone and taking in everything around me and trying to appreciate even more made me happy and helped my brain come around too. I will tell you, the day I got the retirement letter, that was like a huge switch in my brain and body and even though I thought I didn't want it, it was like a huge weight off my soul. I mourned it, I mourned it for a long time, but by the time I got that letter I was good to go.

"Then one day I woke up after a night of drinking and knew I was done with alcohol. I don't know why, but it happened. I didn't see God, and I didn't hear a voice, but I remember going, 'I'm fucking done drinking.'

"I haven't had a drink in four years, and I haven't wanted one. It must have been a higher power because I can't think of another explanation.

"If I had to pick an explanation, maybe it would be seeing my wife really meaning she'd leave this time. But like the other times, I'd gotten sober in the past, it felt nothing like this time. It wasn't easy, but it was easy in a way. I went through that awful detox, again, in my bedroom, and then once I felt better, it was, 'All right. What's up. Let's go. Let's live life.' It was nothing a human being did for me. It wasn't willpower because I'd tried too hard not to drink and always ended up drinking again. It was an obsession that I had to have it and I wasn't going to go on without it.

"It probably made me more spiritual than I ever was. I have always believed in God, but I honestly believed He helped me that day and every day since, and He's always been with me, kept me from killing myself, and dying in a wreck. The therapy also helped me understand myself and let go of the survivor's guilt. I'm a different person than I was before. A better person."

He thought for a moment and continues, "I think a person has to be careful about how they create their identity. If all the focus is in one area, you'll be in for a huge letdown when something changes. That's what happened to me, and it was hard to deal with, but with the support of my family, I did it."

After he retired, Dillon started a new business and has been more successful than he ever thought he could be. He has most definitely grown from his traumas. He believes his spiritual experience saved his life. His love for his wife and family has enriched his own. He connects to the world in a way he could have never imagined. Once he began understanding himself and the course his traumas had propelled him on, he could create a new narrative, new missions, a new course for his life. It wasn't easy, but he is more fulfilled than he ever thought he could be.

CHAPTER 9

BOBBY

Officer Involved Shooting (OIS)

*"Children begin by loving their parents, then they judge them,
sometimes they forgive them."*
OSCAR WILDE

One might think Bobby is shy until he unexpectedly makes eye contact and breaks into a charming smile. He's well-spoken but restrained in revealing his intelligence. He's active and fit and rides a Harley. He also likes carpentry and can distract himself with a variety of activities. Women find him non-threatening and vulnerable. Adorable even. He's introspective and could have been a poet in another life. Ordinary things catch his attention in remarkable ways, and this trait often guides the decisions he makes. He once texted me photos of a solar eclipse he took from a mountaintop. "I wanted to get as close as I could to the sun," he said.

Bobby had a great life. He'd served as a law enforcement officer in a rural office in a large state agency for nearly 30 years and had recently accepted a non-patrol position to wait out the four months until he retired. Patrol was for younger guys.

His career had been relatively uneventful. He had never been involved in an incident that disturbed him for more than a few hours. He'd never discharged his weapon in the line of duty or been in a significant physical altercation. He liked his "ordinary world" and considered himself blessed to have such a pleasant life amidst rural majesty, especially compared to some of his co-workers who'd been divorced, developed alcohol problems, and hated their commanding officers.

His days were predictable. He arrived at the office every morning, enjoyed coffee with his co-workers in the shadow of snow-capped mountains, interacted with the public for a few hours, ate lunch at his favorite burger place, and finished some paperwork. At 5 p.m., he headed home to a pleasant dinner with his wife, Kim, in front of the TV. On his days off, he would hike the nearby majestic peaks or go to the lake for a barbeque. His 15-year marriage had been happy and fulfilled. After retirement, he planned to travel around the US in the new motor home he and Kim had purchased.

Bobby's life was peaceful—mundane. It didn't involve drama or intense emotion or unpleasant thoughts. He made sure of it.

One summer day, a mentally disturbed man in a nearby town asked his estranged wife for visitation with their infant daughter. The mother allowed her ex-husband to take the child for the afternoon. Within hours, she reported that the father had not returned the baby home. Local law enforcement located the father, who claimed to have left the baby asleep on a blanket in his fenced yard while he attended to some chores. When he returned, he said, the baby had disappeared. A massive search was organized. Posters with the baby's photo were plastered on store windows and telephone poles. The FBI became involved. The story was front-page news for weeks. Search and rescue dogs found the baby's binky in a wooded area, but the child seemed to have vanished into thin air. The entire community seemed to be on high alert. As law enforcement investigated, they began to suspect that the father knew more about his daughter's fate than he was letting on. He became the sole person of interest. When his arrest seemed imminent, he went on the run.

The morning of the critical incident, Bobby and his office partner were headed to a local coffee shop for their morning fix of caffeine when a call came from dispatch. A suspect had stolen a car at gunpoint from an elderly couple and was last seen speeding up the freeway towards Bobby's town.

Officers from several law enforcement agencies raced up the freeway in pursuit. At the time, Bobby thought that the small army of officers would find and detain the suspect, and he could go back and finish his cup of coffee. Then word came out over the radio that the suspected car thief was the father of the missing baby.

Since Bobby and his partner were close to the tiny village where the suspect had been sighted, they decided to check it out. When they arrived, police vehicles blocked the streets. Bobby and his partner exited their vehicle and walked through narrow winding streets to help search. Soon, he found himself in a yard surrounded by a small white picket fence. He looked around and initially saw nothing but the hairs on the back of his neck tingled. The thought crossed his mind, "I thought I was going to have fun this morning, not confront a suspect."

Out of the blue, a shot rang out. The baby's father, who was hiding in a carport directly across the street from Bobby's position, discharged his weapon. Bobby was in the line of fire and his only cover was the flimsy fence. Later, as he cognitively processed the scene, he recalled seeing the suspect crouched in the garage, his head lowered. "I saw his face," Bobby said. "The moment his head came up his face distorted. I knew he'd made the decision to die."

Immediately Bobby went into action. Without actively being conscious of it, he drew his service weapon. He doesn't recall initiating firing but thinks he remembers seeing flashes coming from his handgun. His fight or flight response "kicked in" a split second before the visual centers of his brain processed what was happening. The entire incident from the suspect raising his head to Bobby discharging his weapon took no more than one or two seconds. He didn't have time to think; his training took over. Simultaneously, more than a dozen officers from several departments began firing at the suspect. The volley of rifle and handgun shots was deafening and seemed to go on forever.

Why did so many of the officers shoot? Simply, they were responding to a deadly threat. They were in pursuit of a suspect they believed to have killed his own infant daughter. To elude law enforcement, he stole a car at gunpoint from an elderly couple, endangering them. He fled at a high rate of speed, placing everyone on the freeway at risk. He was armed and hiding in a garage in a residential neighborhood with civilians nearby. Without warning, or attempting to give himself up, he began shooting at officers who were searching for him. The suspect was clearly an immediate public threat who could have killed or caused great bodily harm to the officers or civilians. The only option was to neutralize him using deadly force.

Why did they shoot so many rounds? They were in the throes of heightened anxiety and release of adrenaline. Police officers are trained to fire until they've terminated the threat. When an officer is stressed, fewer than half of their rounds may actually hit the target. Under extremely demanding circumstances, sympathetic or reflexive fire can occur even when officers haven't immediately recognized the suspect as a threat. Also, officers are trained to shoot in quick succession when using deadly force. To stop and assess the situation would give the suspect time to harm others. (Andrew, 2020)

The threat was quickly neutralized. In moments, the suspect was declared dead at the scene. There was no chance of resuscitation.

Bobby was immediately engulfed with remorse. He went numb. His weapon, which a moment before had seemed like an extension of himself, felt foreign. It was as if someone else fired it. In reality, he fired to protect himself and other officers. He was also responding to the psychology of the group, and the demands of the critical situation.

In order for a soldier or law enforcement officer to overcome natural resistance to taking another human life, he or she must respond to the demands of authority, conform to the ethos of the group, and have psychological distance from the person they are killing. This diffusion of responsibility allows them to rationalize the need for killing. (Grossman, 1996)

Immediately after, Bobby made a decision that would haunt him thereafter. Because he felt great responsibility and immediate remorse, he crossed the yard and walked into the garage. He looked directly into the suspect's still-opened eyes as the life drained out of them. The act was a final communication that etched into Bobby's brain.

> Human survival depends on us functioning as a tribe. As a result, our brains are built to connect with others, to quickly determine if we are safe or should run away. We are extraordinarily attuned to emotional states of other humans and animals. Even slight changes in position, expression, reaction clue us into the inner workings of other beings. Specialized cells in the cortex called mirror neurons allow us to register emotional state and intentions. In the best of circumstances, our mirror neurons are in synch with another's intentions in a positive way. (van der Kolk, 2014)

When Bobby looked directly into the suspect's eyes, his brain seemed to be hijacked by all the rage, terror, and pain the suspect was experiencing and he was dragged down with him. The image of the suspect lying on the ground, the life fading from his eyes, stayed stuck directly in front of Bobby's line of sight for months. He no longer had psychological distance from the suspect. At that moment, Bobby left his "ordinary" world and was thrust into an unfamiliar internal psychological world full of ambiguities and vulnerabilities.

Like many law enforcement officers, Bobby perceived himself as different and separate from the rest of the human species. He was trained, and accepted, the myth of physical and psychological invulnerability. His job was to run into a threat, conquer it, and render it harmless. Cops may know at some level that they could be hurt or killed in the line of duty, but the actual experience of vulnerability doesn't often come until after a critical incident.

On a deep level, Bobby had always thought of himself as a good person, one who took the job to help and protect people. But if he was a good person, how could he have shot the suspect? Once he looked into the man's eyes, the psychological distance vanished, and he could not rationalize or excuse his actions. He became angry with himself for reacting without thinking. He was overwhelmed with anguish and began to hate himself. He also felt enraged with the suspect for placing him in the position to have to shoot him.

According to the International Association of Chiefs of Police (IACP, 2016), an officer-involved-shooting (OIS) is perhaps the most traumatic event an officer will face during service. An OIS will trigger psychological, cognitive, physical, and emotional effects that overwhelm normal coping strategies. Reactions are as unique as the individual officer but may last weeks to months after the event. Most return to a balanced and healthy emotional state, but some become stuck. Bobby's recovery stalled and he began circling the drain.

His life before the shooting had been laughter, comfort, and love. Now, he was plagued by graphic nightmares of death—sprays of blood and brains as he had witnessed during the shooting. In one dream he was free-falling with no parachute. Relationships that had brought him joy were now a source of deep pain. Human contact made him feel claustrophobic, trapped, like he was drowning. In one bizarre event, he was watching a movie in which a character "flatlined." Suddenly, Bobby flashed on the shooting except rather than watching the suspect, his perspective changed so that he was inside the man's body, looking out during the last moments before he died.

And the shooting and whereabouts of the baby were still in the daily news. The mother offered a reward for her baby's safe return. She was never found.

He began to isolate and drink. He stopped caring. He started to fight with Kim. He couldn't tolerate being close—it was too frightening to feel vulnerable. His libido tanked. His confidence was shattered. His expectations of himself as a just and ethical person disappeared. He felt "off." His soul seemed to evaporate. He said, "When I look in the mirror, my face is so distorted I don't even recognize myself."

He could no longer remain in the relative comfort of the ordinary first responder world. He stopped talking to his co-workers, to his wife, to everyone. He avoided therapy. How could he explain what that shooting had taken from him? The rest of the world seemed to think the suspect killed his baby and ultimately got what he deserved. Bobby developed both intense hatred and a deep empathy for him. How tortured must the man have been after he killed his baby daughter to essentially commit suicide by cop? Yet the suspect's decision had taken everything away from Bobby. Bobby also grieved terribly for the baby as if she was his own child.

He knew he had to get away from the reminders, the press, everyone.

Bobby waited out the days until his retirement. With little notice, he told his wife that he planned to hike the 2200-mile Appalachian Trail—without her. He didn't tell her that every time they had the slightest disagreement, her face turned into the face of the suspect. He had to get away.

As soon as the weather warmed, he flew to the East Coast. He told himself that he needed the space, an adventure to clear his mind. Only later did he realize that although the Appalachian Trail took him physically away from the triggers that reminded him of the shooting, he couldn't escape what was going on in the space between his ears. The intrusive recollections, the dreams of loud explosions and white lights, and how the panic attacks stayed with him every moment.

Bobby explained, "The day of the shooting the vault in my mind where I kept all those emotions broke open. I hadn't been emotionally connected to things, people, events that caused emotion. After the shooting, the emotions flooded out and I was drowning in them."

The Appalachian Trail did offer him anonymity and a guidebook to another life path. Yet, he still didn't want to admit to anyone he met that he had a problem. Along the way, he met people who accepted him for who he was at that moment—a hiker on the trail. He said, "All it takes is a nice smile and a glitter in your eye to hide how broken you feel."

Still, he was haunted with thoughts about what might have been. He ruminated and told himself, "If I had waited another half-second to shoot, I wouldn't be in this pain. My wife wouldn't be in this pain." Although he feared being alone, he wanted his wife to leave so he wouldn't have to think of the suspect. And the most tragic thought of all to Bobby, "Now no one will know where the baby is, not her mom, not her grandparents, because the police shot and killed her father."

Gradually, the trail turned into an emotional experience. He met a woman who taught him about the Bible. He searched for God in the wilderness.

He slowly became comfortable telling his story—not in detail—but a bit at a time as a test of what his new friends could handle. He developed some insight into his symptoms. He established goals. He fell in love. He actively thought of how he could recover from the trauma, although he didn't know he had barely taken his first step in the journey. He had a thought previously unfamiliar to him, "I'm doing this alone, the same as I did in my childhood."

Bobby's freedom and experiences with people who didn't know or judge him helped him realize, at least on a cognitive level, that he had shot the suspect not to kill, but to save himself and the other peace officers. This offered a small degree of comfort, but the man's eyes kept materializing right in his line of sight, as if judging him. And at the same time, he was enraged with the man. "Why did he make me do it?" he asked. Morally, he was conflicted, and there remained a shadow inside his soul that embodied shame, weakness, unworthiness, and inferiority. He said, "Right then, the posttraumatic stress injury owned me."

Months later, he flew back to the West Coast. His wife was there to greet him, but he barely recognized her, physically or emotionally. Their relationship was ultimately another victim of the incident.

Without the Appalachian Trail, Bobby had no guidebook. He was lost, disoriented. He felt claustrophobic and lost his hearing. When he was alone, he felt himself "going off the deep end." He went camping by himself and woke up sensing someone was in his truck. No one was there. He saw the image of the suspect lying on the ground in front of him. There were days when he couldn't stop crying.

He began to drink even more than before. He became involved with women outside his marriage. He broke his wife's heart, and as much as he hated himself, he couldn't stop from doing it again and again.

Bobby eventually applied to the West Coast Posttrauma Retreat, the 6-day inpatient program for first responders plagued with PTSD. Before he went, he had a dream of being in a plane spiraling to the ground. He worried that the people he met there would judge him.

WCPR participants are advised to talk about the thing they most don't want to bring up. Clients learn that one may never know who will develop PTSD, but therapists do know that childhood trauma plays a role. Bobby realized he had buried that "thing" for years, but now he had to build the courage to explore his demons

Bobby recalled that his early childhood was secure and happy. His parents seemed to be in love. He had a younger brother. It was the life he tried to recreate as an adult. He remembered the day he found out his mother was pregnant. It was a happy day. He was four years old.

Tragically, his little sister, Angel, was born horribly deformed and challenged, physically and mentally. As time went by, she began consuming all his parents' time and energy. Bobby struggled to admit the truth about what happened next. The young Bobby became highly resentful of his little sister. He tried to bid for his mother's attention, but she became depressed and emotionally unavailable. She began taking pills to cope. His father climbed into the bottle and spent more and more time away from home. Bobby began to go into Angel's bedroom every morning and poke her in the eye, with the intent of hurting her. When Angel laughed at the attention, he would poke her harder.

Then, when he was five years old, the worst happened. One morning Bobby heard his mother shriek in agony. Overnight, Angel's oversized head had become stuck in the slats of the crib, and she was strangled. In Bobby's child-mind, he had killed her.

His parents soon divorced. His mother became a prescription medication addict. His father remarried to a woman Bobby and his brother referred to as the "step-monster" who locked the boys out of the house and refused to feed them when their father was away at work. Life at home was hell. He learned to never ask for help or to allow himself to feel weak because no one would come to help him. In their grief, his parents had abandoned him emotionally. The only way he could cope with his grief, anger, and guilt was to lock it up in the "vault of his mind." He almost made it to retirement until the OIS broke the lock on the vault and all the festering emotions flooded out.

At the age of 18, Bobby escaped an unhappy home life to join the service. After a stateside tour of duty, the logical choice had been to apply to become a cop. It was a career that allowed him to help others. He was happy to leave behind the dysfunction in his family of origin and find a new family that valued him and gave him a sense of purpose.

After facing the shame he felt about Angel, he realized he was ready to continue with therapy. During one session, his therapist used EMDR, a treatment used to treat PTSD. Bobby had an epiphany. The baby who disappeared at the hands of her father had become, in his mind, Angel: an innocent child at the mercy of someone who should have been protecting her.

In Bobby's mind, when he looked into the dying suspect's eyes, he made an intense, empathetic, devastating connection. The "dots" in Bobby's mind began to connect. He became the equivalent of the "monster" he shot. Evil, hateful, irresponsible.

His intense emotional reaction to the suspect echoed the disgust he felt about his childhood misbehavior toward his sister, Angel. All those years, he'd hidden Angel and his shameful secret from his friends, his colleagues, his wife, and himself. The secret he buried crippled him emotionally, smothered him in shame, and denied him true intimacy. Not until he explored his childhood vulnerabilities could he recognize the connection between his reaction to the OIS and the feelings he had suppressed.

Ironically, connecting the fact that he blamed himself for Angel's death with the morbid association he had made with the dying suspect by looking into his eyes led him to develop greater concern for social issues and a deep need to make a difference in the world. He realized he wanted to rescue and to be rescued. He had a deep emotional connection to people who had experienced trauma. "We understand each other." Now he needed to develop the strength to ask for help.

The injured Bobby underwent a figurative death and began a transformation into a true self. With new wisdom, his triggers held less power over him. His anxiety lessened. His emotions no longer controlled him. His need for alcohol decreased. He started on the road to self-forgiveness for the OIS.

The concept of forgiveness is a difficult one, perhaps even more so for cops who think in terms of black and white. But according to Luskin (2010), holding onto resentments increases stress and negatively impacts our physical and mental health. Forgiveness in Luskin's view doesn't mean condoning bad behavior or forgetting that someone (including yourself) has let you down or harmed you. What it does mean is working on making a choice to not allow the anger, hurt, or frustration to rule or ruin our lives. In other words, learning to let it go.

Most people are self-critical. We are hard-wired to be vigilant about making mistakes. First responders' mistakes or misjudgments may have grave, deadly consequences as we have seen in the news in recent years. Nonetheless, a lack of self-forgiveness can lead to guilt, shame, anxiety, depression, and great suffering.

Bobby learned he had the opportunity to forgive not only his parents for their emotional abandonment of him after his baby sister, Angel, died. He also had a choice of deciding whether he was ready to forgive himself for his jealousy and childish attempts to inflict pain on Angel in addition to returning fire and shooting the subject.

Letting go is intensely difficult, but with perseverance and motivation, it can be done. In an interview with Carole Pertofsky of Stanford School of Medicine (Shumake, 2019), one aspect of self-forgiveness is to have the same compassion for yourself as you would for a friend in the same circumstances. Being aware of unenforceable standards you set up for yourself and others, such as never making a mistake or never acting on poor judgment, is a step. Bobby was a small child when he "poked" his sister with no mature understanding of his resentment of her or how to handle it in a mature manner. In the OIS, he found himself in a situation in which his life and the life of his colleagues were at risk from the suspect shooting at them. He did not have a few seconds to make another choice about discharging his firearm. He reacted from his training. And the consequences of holding himself to impossible standards nearly destroyed him.

When an error can't be fixed, guilt and regret can be very painful. The best option may be to humble yourself and accept your culpability. Then try to learn from your experience.

We'll leave Bobby standing at his parents' gravesite in a green, leafy cemetery on the East Coast. Angel's grave lies between them. He had been thinking about how his parents felt when Angel died.

"My path of loss—my struggle—is like my parents," he explained. "Part of my child-self wished that Angel would die so my mother would pay attention to me, then when it happened, I lost everything. We all did. We lost Angel and we lost our family and ourselves." Bobby smiled. "My parents were imperfect. They couldn't hold it together after Angel died. But they know what I did to Angel. I'm certain she told them when they died and joined her."

"Have they forgiven you?" I asked.

He thought for a moment. "Yes. They have. I was a little boy, and I was hurt and scared. They don't blame me. They want me to understand that. And Angel loved getting attention from her big brother, even if he was mean."

"That sounds like pretty typical siblings," I said. "Have you forgiven your parents for not being able to cope?"

"I've forgiven my mom." He looked away. "I'm still working on my dad." He added, "And I can fanaticize Angel as growing up healthy and having kids."

That's true progress, I thought.

The rest of the story: Bobby never had children for fear he would harm them even though he loves children and has longed for them. Shortly before he told me his story, he witnessed the birth of his grandniece. Bobby's journey of growth is not over. He needs to learn to trust others and himself in relationships, but from the look on his face when he pulled out his phone and showed me his grandniece's picture, I could tell he was in love.

CHAPTER 10

HARRIETT

Extremely Personal Incidents

"One of the deep secrets of life is that all that is really worth doing is what we do for others."
LEWIS CARROLL

"Fear is met and destroyed with courage."
JAMES M. BELL

Harriet is tall, slender, and blue-eyed with a shock of short curly hair. She walks with a confident swagger. Command presence oozes from her yet she has a soft side that inspires trust in emotionally vulnerable children and all kinds of animals.

Harriet decided she wanted to be a cop when she was in grade school after a sheriff's deputy arrested the man who was molesting her. After she graduated from college and the police academy, she found a job as one of the few females in her department. She was promoted to detective and assigned to sex crimes. Her childhood experience as a victim of sexual abuse gave her an intuitive gift for interviewing young victims and taught her how to read the behavior of sex offenders.

I first met Harriet after she had been involved in an officer-involved shooting (OIS) in which the suspect aimed a handgun at officers and pulled the trigger. He was subsequently shot and killed by the officers. My interview with her was part of her department's Critical Incident Stress Management (CISM) offered to officers who have been involved in shootings.

Harriet's role in the incident was to locate and subdue the suspect with a beanbag, a small fabric pillow filled with lead shot weighing about an ounce and a half. The bean bag is expelled from a 12-gauge shotgun at about 250 feet per second and is considered a "less lethal" weapon used when apprehending suspects. Harriett was not one of the officers who fired the fatal rounds used that day that neutralized the suspect. However, the most difficult aspect of the incident was that she didn't have time to deploy her firearm to protect the other officers who were in danger of being shot by the suspect. This thought had stayed in the back of her mind and bit by bit had eroded her confidence that she was a good cop.

After the CISM, Harriett felt confident enough to return to work. Then, several months later, she thought she was having a heart attack. She went to the emergency room. Her heart was in arrhythmia and the ER doctor made an immediate referral to a cardiologist for evaluation of cardiovascular disease. Although the results didn't reveal a physiological cause for the heart problems, Harriett began having increasing episodes of a racing pulse, sleeplessness, nightmares, tightness in her chest, trouble concentrating, and outbursts of anger.

> Somatic symptoms for which there are no obvious basis are the hallmark of traumatized individuals along with intrusive thoughts, hyperreactivity, and avoidance of situations that are reminiscent of the trauma.

Within six months of the shooting, she was back in my office. "I think I'm having panic attacks, Doc. I'm jumpy at everything, everyone pisses me off, and I don't know what the matter is." She confessed that she'd been hitting the bottle hard and drinking to inebriation on her days off. Her symptoms were consistent with a posttraumatic stress injury. The heavy drinking was most certainly not helping her.

Harriett reported that, in addition to her panic and anger, she felt emotionally numb. People annoyed her—the public had caused her grief for some time, but now, even her loved ones bothered her. She was emotionally detached from her family and partner, who complained that he "just wanted the old Harriett back." She didn't seem to be able to find any joy in her relationships. As a result, she developed negative, judgmental ideas about herself. She thought there must be something wrong with her to be unable to emotionally connect with her loved ones anymore.

Even worse were the sensations and images. Bloody car crashes and crime scenes. The smell of rotten eggs from gunpowder and the metallic odor of blood. I thought about the OIS and wondered if that was the source of her emotional pain. Perhaps the CISM hadn't been enough to help her resolve the incident.

We discussed the OIS in great detail. With talking and stress reduction techniques, Harriett finally reached some understanding. "The volume got turned up on everything—the fear, the stress, being afraid for everyone, that they would get hurt," Harriett said. "I was in charge of keeping my people safe that night, and I couldn't get out my weapon fast enough after I deployed the bean bag. They could have been killed from my slowness to act. I didn't protect my people."

The understanding helped Harriett feel less numb. However, the shooting didn't seem to be the sole cause of her symptoms. We tried some other trauma reduction techniques, and she began to get in touch with intense anger. At one point, she became so tearful she couldn't speak. "I . . . want . . . it . . . out!" was all she could squeak out. Her eyes were full of desperation and fear. Frankly, I was a bit frightened for her. She was able to describe some "foggy" videos in her head but could not consciously access them.

I referred her to the West Coast Posttrauma Retreat (WCPR) for an intensive six-day education and extended Critical Incident Stress Debriefing session in hopes that she could make more progress. The session included Eye Movement Desensitization Reprocessing (EMDR), a method of treating of traumatic memories included EMDR a method of treating traumatic memories.

Harriett was initially nervous about going to WCPR and "spilling her guts." Nonetheless, she was determined to get better. She accepted the challenge, crossed the threshold, met mentors, made friends and allies, and seized the sword of knowledge.

During her work at WCPR, she gained insight into the role her family played in her reaction to the shooting. As the oldest child, her role was to protect her younger siblings from the dysfunction in her family of origin. When she left home, she was both relieved to be free and ashamed that she had abandoned her siblings. The shame and guilt settled in a part of her mind that she attempted to wall off. It worked until the officer-involved shooting. The wall crumbled when she was unable to pull her weapon fast enough to protect the other officers—just as she hadn't been able to protect her siblings. The dishonor she felt after the OIS directly mirrored the emotions she experienced when she left home. Harriett had not realized the connection between the two situations until therapy helped her "connect the dots."

However, when it came to the EMDR performed at WCPR, which generally helps clients gain self-knowledge and reduce the emotional punch of their PTSI symptoms, she drew a blank. Very literally. She was unable to come up with an image to work on. She described her mind like a "black hole"—nothing was escaping from it. She was left feeling lost and numb.

When she returned home, her numbness began to lift. She reduced her drinking, started yoga, and kept in contact with people she met at WCPR. The disturbing images in her head seemed "farther away" but continued to distress her. As a cloud of pain remained, we began to explore more of her childhood.

Early in therapy, she had mentioned that a family friend molested her but downplayed the impact it made on her. The man had been arrested but skipped bail and never went to trial. She minimized the situation because she believed it had inspired her to enter law enforcement.

She also minimized the time she spent serving as a juvenile sex crimes investigator six years prior to when I met her. She said, "It was just another part of the job."

She described symptoms of sadness, emptiness, and nothingness. She avoided physical contact and physical intimacy, even cuddling with her partner. Her shoulders were tense. She felt unsafe, even at the local market. One day, she froze at the self-checkout and ran out, leaving her groceries behind.

"Why couldn't I just ask for help with the stupid check-out machine?" she asked.

"Do you ever ask for help?" I asked.

She glared at me. "Therapy sucks! Asking for help sucks."

"Not accepting anyone's help could be a big part of your problem," I said.

Avoiding physical contact and not trusting others to be there to help her were consistent with a history of sexual abuse. But Harriett was reluctant to delve into the details of the abuse. Her alcohol abuse hadn't helped her memory or her ability to process the memories. The reason she liked alcohol, she said, was that it helped her sleep and reduced her nightmares.

In truth, alcohol use interferes with sleep and can contribute to PTSD. Alcohol is a seductive sedative that tricks people into thinking they sleep better because they fall asleep quickly. However, they have less REM sleep, the part of sleep during which we dream. REM is important in the processing of traumatic memories. Lack of REM sleep can disrupt sleep-dependent emotional memory consolidation and integration trauma and exacerbate symptoms of PTSD. (Pace-Schott et al, 2015)

But before we tackled Harriett's alcohol problem, we needed to go back further.

Harriett was the oldest of three "latch key" kids. She was responsible for the younger two because her parents were working and gone from the home. Her father traveled and was away for weeks at a time, and when he was home, he preferred working in his shop to spending time with his family. Her mother, chronically unhappy and depressed, made everyone else miserable. The lack of affection and validation in her home, coupled with stifling responsibilities made Harriett resentful and angry. She began hanging out at the home of a schoolmate and spending as much time there as possible.

Her friend's uncle lived in her family's garage. He seemed like a fun grown-up. At first, he invited Harriett into his room to watch scary movies. Then he bought her a few treats—candy, the soft drinks she wasn't allowed to have at home. He initiated touch. It felt good. She didn't get it at home, and he seemed to genuinely like her. He graduated to sexual touching, even when her friend was in the room. He taught her how to give him oral sex. Harriett was confused. She was uncomfortable and grossed out, but she didn't want the attention to stop.

Finally, she told her mother. Her mother called law enforcement. The uncle was arrested. Then all hell broke loose. Her friend's parents blamed Harriett and called her a liar. She was forbidden to see her friend, whose family had offered her the stability and validation she craved.

Suddenly, her parents became emotional and overly protective but were ineffective in comforting her. She didn't know how to cope with their unfamiliar behavior—as the responsible one in the family, she thought she had to make her parents feel better. The roots of her guilt and shame began at this time in her life. "Why did I keep going over there?" she asked herself. "Why did I let that man touch me?"

She testified in court at his arraignment. He made bail and skipped town. She was terrified he would come and get her. She developed panic attacks and her parents took her to a counselor. She was not able to open up.

She took her first drink about a year after her molester skipped bail and disappeared. She was 15. The first time she took a few sips of beer at a party she felt relaxed and acknowledged for the first time in years. The second time she passed out drunk. She began to get drunk every weekend, and eventually nearly every night. She graduated from beer to whiskey and was well on her way to a drinking problem by the time she was in her 20s.

Despite her troubles, Harriett is at some level an optimist. Reflecting on the horrors of her childhood she said, "The one thing that I learned from being molested was to be a defender of abused kids."

She grew up with that goal and became a police officer. And as you might have predicted from her ingrained urge to protect, her hatred of child abusers, and her need to right wrongs, she became an investigator of sex crimes. In particular, sex crimes involving children. After a few years of reviewing hundreds of videos of children involved in sexual relationships with adults and interviewing kids who had been molested, she lost her ability to shut out the images. Her personality began to change. She found herself angry at everyone. When it came to perpetrators, she became enraged. Even in sleep, she could not get away from the images of babies being raped.

> Cumulative stress is inevitable in some jobs, and no matter how much a first responder wants to deny personal vulnerabilities and succeed at a job, there are some jobs that have a definite shelf life. One of the most difficult positions in law enforcement, perhaps more stressful than patrol, homicide detective, and even SWAT, is the job of investigating sex crimes, especially those involving children. Interviewing helpless young victims, looking through thousands of child porn photos, and watching hundreds of films showing children being molested is emotionally wrenching. These officers rarely escape feelings of helplessness, futility, and emotional numbness.

One case in particular haunted Harriett. "It really fucked me up," she said. "The little girl was no more than five-years-old. Her parents were tweakers. They needed money for drugs. They filmed her and trafficked their daughter out of the seedy motel where they lived. Now, I can't even drive down that street without feeling sick and shaky, like I'm going vomit."

One image intruded constantly directly in front of Harriett's eyes—a video of the little girl masturbating. "She was looking into the camera. She knew exactly what they wanted her to do. Her vagina was all misshapen and I could tell that she'd been used over and over. Her eyes were without a soul.

"When I saw that, my soul evaporated." Her voice wavered and she seemed to be staring into a void. "I've never been like this."

We tried EMDR again. The session was one of the most unusual I've witnessed.

We prepared for the session by creating a safe place where she could go in her mind should the process become too intense. Then we discussed her most disturbing symptoms: chronic tension and crippling guilt. She had been left lost and numb after the previous EMDR session and wanted to focus on the most painful incident in her mind—the molestation of the little girl. She identified her negative thought: "I abandoned her like my siblings. I should have been able to save her."

> Of course, she was not at fault for what happened to the child, and she did help her by investigating the case, but her statements represented the emotions that still existed.

Then, we picked a positive statement that she wanted to believe instead of the negative thought. She had a hard time with that one, but finally chose "I did what I could and she's okay." She didn't completely feel the statement was true but decided to go with it.

Next, we discussed the usual physical sensations of tightness in her chest, feeling sick to her stomach, and emotional numbness. The intensity of her physical symptoms was highly disturbing and stressful. I reassured her and said I would be there for her during the entire session.

We moved into the desensitization phase. We used tactile bilateral stimulation to facilitate the process. Almost immediately, Harriett stiffened and became mute. She looked terrified. Her eyes widened. She stared straight ahead. Long minutes passed and she didn't move. Finally, she looked at me with flat stunned eyes.

"Her eyes turned black," she said. "The girl's eyes turned black. I think the other investigator saw it."

The story came out agonizing piece by piece. Harriett had been so frightened at what happened while interviewing the little girl that she had blocked the memory. Not only was she frightened of the incident, but she was terrified of the girl. In fact, the girl, after being abruptly removed from her parents during an intense entry into her home by law enforcement, was undoubtedly terrified to talk to Harriett about what her parents had done. Even though they sold her little body for drugs, they were her parents, and if she lost them, what would happen to her? Even at that young age, she understood she had to rely on her parents to keep her alive.

Why do abused children commonly protect their caretakers even if they have been horribly hurt by them? These children may show disorganized attachment: they show both a need for and a fear of their caregiver. The explanation: the infant brain is hardwired for survival. The ability to bond with a caregiver is a strong biological imperative. Once that bond is formed with a caretaker, it is practically impossible to break. This makes sense—caregivers must protect children to keep them alive. Children run to their caregivers/protectors for comfort when scared or hurt. Simply, painful experiences that would normally trigger the release of stress hormones in the child are assuaged by the presence of the caregiver.

But what happens when the caregiver is the source of danger or hurt? Unfortunately, the structures in the brain that suppress fear and pain in the child when comforted by a caregiver still operate the same—they extinguish pain and fear, even the memories associated with trauma, even though the caregiver is the cause of the trauma. (Sullivan and Lasley, 2010)

Harriett dreaded talking about her experience interviewing the girl because it seemed so irrational and bizarre. She wondered if she might be crazy. She didn't feel safe even saying the words she felt, and I had to reassure her she was sane.

Harriett knew she felt intensely drawn to the young girl and was almost obsessed with her case. The girl's story echoed Harriett's personal experience as a child. When she looked deeply into her eyes, they reflected her own fear and pain. And then the girl's eyes seemed to turn black. Harriett felt the "force of evil." She explained, "I felt evil pass from the girl's eyes into my soul."

At first, Harriett felt deep empathy for the girl in the interview. She thought they were in synch. She understood her fear and confusion and how difficult it would be for her to reveal her parents' horrible abuse of her. But then she remembered how her life had turned upside-down when she exposed her abuser, leaving her alone and terrified. Suddenly, Harriet was sucked into the emotional maelstrom of the girl's rage and terror: her anger at her abusers and her fear that they would abandon her.

What happened?

There are neurons in our brains that allow us to "read" others by merely observing them. These neurons, called *mirror neurons* allow us to perceive the emotional state and even intentions of others—that is mirror them. Mirror neurons facilitate our understanding of others, as well as our empathy toward them. They are rather remarkable and seem to occur in other animals besides humans. (Have you ever had your cat "telegraph" to you it's time to eat?)

The good thing about mirror neurons is they make it possible to experience understanding of others' positive emotions, and help discern if they are friend or foe, in a good mood or a foul one. They can even give us clues as to what another person's physical actions will be.

The downside of mirror neurons is that they make us susceptible to negative emotions as well. The girl's intense rage and fear burst like a shotgun into Harriett's brain. Could Harriett's mirror neurons have been activated?

Harriett froze in the interview and then ran out of the room. Her partner, who had been observing the interview, said, "That was intense." In Harriett's mind, that evil was still inhabiting her soul and she became convinced she was crazy. Later, she told me, "When we looked into each other's eyes, it sucked my soul out. It was the most horrifying thing. I never experienced anything like that before." The girl's eyes triggered a full-blown flashback.

During a flashback, the Broca's area of the brain shuts down. The Broca's area is a speech center of the brain located on the left side. The left brain, or the linguistic, sequential, and analytical brain, is in charge of verbal communication. When it's offline, experiences can't be organized into a logical sequence, wiping out the ability to identify cause and effect, or create a narrative about our actions or the future. When the Broca's area goes dark, perceptions, thoughts, and feelings can't be translated into words.

On the other hand, the right brain communicates nonverbally. It reacts to facial expressions, voices, and body language. It stores memories of sensations, touch, sound, smell, and the emotions they evoke. During a flashback, the emotional right brain reacts as if the traumatic event is still happening.

To add to the terror, another region, Brodmann's area 19, which is located in the visual cortex of the brain and registers images when they first enter the brain, comes into play. Under normal conditions, these images dissipate, but in a flashback, Brodmann's area 19 is activated, and horrifying images are experienced as if they are in the present.

Harriett lost her ability to speak. Terrifying images flooded her mind. Her left hemisphere shut down and she was left reexperiencing and reenacting the presence of evil as she had during her own molest with no way of comprehending what was happening to her. She had to flee the interview until she could regain her composure.

Harriett had spent years suppressing her inner turmoil. Her conscious mind went on with life as if nothing had happened, yet her emotional brain was in high gear and her body was constantly in a state of alarm. No wonder she became a cop! All those stress hormones needed something to do. And they kept doing their job, through officer-involved shootings, grisly traffic accidents, arresting all kinds of criminals, until she was overloaded. She tried to dull her increasing inability to cope with alcohol. And when that stopped working, she crashed.

Now, all her statements about "wanting it out" made sense. Her inability to talk about her molestation, her drinking to suppress her emotions, and her emotional numbness. She had organized her life around trying to avoid her traumatic memories. She abused alcohol to block out her unbearable memories. Reliving her trauma was in a sense worse than the actual events—the molesting had stopped, but the intrusive memories, body sensations, and flashbacks could occur at any time.

In her mind, Harriett imagined herself as guilty as her molester. She despised herself for going over to his house night after night knowing what would happen. Her shame was bottomless. She couldn't allow herself to feel love and happiness without feeling the rage and paradoxical gratitude she had felt for her molester.

I once asked Harriett about how she perceived her looks. "I don't know," she said. "I never look at myself in the mirror."

Harriett always seemed physically stiff. Her movements were not fluid even when she was in a relaxed situation. At the beginning of every session, she stared at me silently and without expression for a few moments. I felt awkward, like I was making her feel uncomfortable.

Then I went to my Aunt Judith's funeral. She was my mother's younger sister and had inherited family movies from their childhood that I had never seen. I watched my mother on film as a young girl playing, her body freely moving, her face expressive, joy in her eyes. I had never known my mother like this. The mother I knew was oddly off balance. Her eyes never smiled, and her face always seemed pinched, like there was tension in her jaw. What had happened in her life to cause this?

My mother's mother had died tragically and unexpectedly when she was 15. Her father became an alcoholic and never talked about my grandmother's death. My mother was basically left on her own to negotiate life, go to college, and have a family. After she married and became pregnant with me, her doctors told her I wouldn't make it to term. They prescribed DES (diethylstilbestrol) to prevent miscarriage. I was born early at three pounds. I was placed in an incubator, and she was told that I was as likely to die as to live. She was afraid to hold me or allow herself to become attached.

I can't imagine the agony she must have gone through to have lost her mother at a tender age and then be faced with losing her only child. Even sadder, she could never discuss her pregnancy or my birth with me with any modulated emotion. I once saw an article about the effects of DES on children whose mothers took it to avoid miscarriage. I casually and innocently mentioned it to my mother without realizing she had taken it when she was pregnant with me. She flew into a rage and broke down. "I was trying to save your life," she sobbed. I soon learned that asking about my infancy was off the table. She couldn't identify, much less modulate, her emotions to talk about those painful moments when she lived in terror that I'd die.

When I saw those movies of my mother filmed before her mother died, I finally understood why my mother had emotionally shut down. She suffered from alexithymia—she could not put her feelings into words. She had learned to shut down her emotional pain to the extent that she did not know what she was feeling. She denied her feelings even though they were written on her face. Under stress, she either spaced out or became frustrated. Until later in life, she was afraid to hug me or to interact with our family in an emotionally available manner.

Harriett and my mother had the same vacancy in their eyes, mask-like expressions, and unawareness of physical feelings. Each was holding trauma in their bodies. They couldn't access their feelings well enough to express their needs. The enemy had become not the molester or the death, but their own physical sensations that made them feel terrified and alone. Their safety vanished when the fear and helplessness showed up. They spent enormous energy holding themselves together, trying not to cry, trying not to feel.

Harriett didn't become a cop by accident. Nor did she choose coincidentally to work with child victims of sexual trauma. Freud called it repetition compulsion—a pattern whereby a person repetitively acts out behaviors representing traumatic events earlier in life. We now know that strong emotions can block pain through the action of endorphins, the chemicals released by the body in reaction to stress and pain. Endorphins act on the opiate receptors in our brains to create pleasurable feelings and thereby reduce pain and stress. Simply, through this action, re-exposure to stress can provide relief from anxiety.

The second EMDR session was the beginning of a change for Harriett. Once she had processed the horror and rage, she saw in the little girl's eyes and recognized the emotions as the part of her own self that she dissociated from, she began to integrate her split-off parts into the narrative of her life. As she realized the harmful effects of alcohol, Harriett began to slow down her drinking. She had attended an AA meeting at WCPR and continued with an online version for law enforcement officers. She began to open up to the valuable people in her life, including her siblings. Sharing their mutual trauma, the things they had never talked about, was validating to her. Harriett also courageously confronted her parents about her childhood.

She realized the OIS was not the issue, although it had gotten her into therapy. "After the shooting, the volume got turned up on everything. The fear and stress came out. I was afraid for everyone, and it was my job to keep them safe." The reaction she had to the shooting seemed to knock a hole in the well-defended wall she constructed while she was working sex abuse cases. And when that broke, so did she, at least until she was able to work through the overwhelming trauma she was holding in her body.

She subsequently decided to retire from law enforcement but like a true adrenaline junky, was concerned she would be bored. Knowing she needed a purpose to feel whole, I encouraged her to find another way to help children. Soon she came back with a brilliant plan.

She had seen a flyer for a rescue horse ranch. She signed up as a client and attended a session.

"That sounds fun," I said. "What did you do there?"

"I groomed the horse and rode him." Her eyes twinkled. "And then, good cop that I am, I shoveled his shit."

I laughed out loud. I had never seen her eyes light up before. Harriett was definitely headed in the right direction.

The rescue horse ranch also ran a rehabilitative program for at-risk children. Before long, Harriett was volunteering as a counselor helping the kids touch, groom, ride, and take care of the horses. Kids instinctually opened up to her. One week two of them revealed for the first time that they'd been sexually abused. Harriett said, "I was totally triggered, but I handled it, and we finished the session no problem."

"It's not that you're triggered—it's how you handle being triggered," I told her.

She continued to train with a "Heroes" program to learn leadership through horsemanship. Part of her training was nonverbal communication and working with "the heart" of the horse. The physical contact she had with the horses seemed to physically transform her. Her movements were freer, she made eye contact, she smiled. She hoped to someday buy some land and start her own program helping kids and first responders learn "the heart" of horses.

She told me a story that happened years ago before she dealt with her PTSD. Her niece was badly injured in an accident. The rest of the family was in tears. Harriett was stoic and didn't show any compassion. Finally, her mother confronted her. "Don't you feel anything? Why can't you just not be a cop for once?"

Harriett said, "But now I have feeling. The Heroes horse program took away my numbness. All of us have been through trauma—the kids I work with, the rescue horses, and me. We're in it to help each other. I guess that's the reason it's so powerful."

Harriett understands that although her posttraumatic stress injury was intensely painful, it gave her a new life, meaning, and understanding of her purpose. Without the traumas, she would not have developed the tools to fully appreciate life. Her face is bright with joy, and it moves with her moods rather than appearing mask-like and immobile. While Harriett thought leaving her law enforcement career meant her life was over, instead, she has found even greater purpose with her work with children and horses.

She is transformed.

GETTING ON WITH THE REST OF YOUR LIFE

CHAPTER 11

INTERVENTIONS FOR DEALING WITH PTSD AND TRIGGERS

This chapter delineates the most well-known and effective interventions and treatment centers for posttraumatic stress injuries.

CRITICAL INCIDENT STRESS MANAGEMENT (CISM)

CISM, developed by Mitchell (2020), is a comprehensive, integrative, multicomponent, structured system developed to respond to and mitigate normal psychological and emotional symptoms in those impacted by traumatic events. The process is designed to provide interventions throughout the phases of a critical incident and afterward, and to help individuals and groups share their experiences, vent emotions, learn about stress symptoms and reduction thereof, and receive a referral for further help if necessary. It was originally used for first responders but has been adapted for use in individuals, small functional groups, large groups, families, organizations, and communities impacted by disasters and other traumatic events. The use of CISM after a critical incident can dramatically reduce posttraumatic stress symptoms.

AMERICAN PSYCHOLOGICAL ASSOCIATION

The American Psychological Association (2020) lists current therapies for PTSD along with recommendations and case history examples at https://www.apa.org/ptsd-guideline/treatments.

The APA (2020) strongly recommends the following therapies:

Cognitive Behavioral Therapy

Cognitive behavioral therapy focuses on the relationships among thoughts, feelings, and behaviors; targets current problems and symptoms; and focuses on changing patterns of behaviors, thoughts, and feelings that lead to difficulties in functioning. Cognitive behavioral therapy notes how changes in any one domain can improve functioning in the other domains. For example, altering a person's unhelpful thinking can lead to healthier behaviors and improved emotion regulation. It is typically delivered over 12-16 sessions in either individual or group format.

Cognitive Processing Therapy

Cognitive processing therapy is a specific type of cognitive behavioral therapy that helps patients learn how to modify, challenge, and reframe negative and unhelpful beliefs related to the trauma. CPT is generally delivered over 12 sessions in which the patient creates a new understanding and conceptualization of the traumatic event to reduce its ongoing negative effects on current life.

Cognitive Therapy

Derived from cognitive behavioral therapy, cognitive therapy entails modifying the pessimistic evaluations and memories of trauma, with the goal of interrupting the disturbing behavioral and/or thought patterns that have been interfering in the person's daily life. It is typically delivered in weekly sessions over three months individually or in groups.

Prolonged Exposure

Prolonged exposure is a specific type of cognitive behavioral therapy that teaches individuals to gradually approach trauma-related memories, feelings, and situations. By facing what has been avoided, a person learns that the trauma-related memories and cues are not dangerous and do not need to be avoided. PE is typically provided over a period of about three months with weekly individual sessions. Sixty- to 120-minute sessions are usually needed for the individual to engage in exposure and sufficiently process the experience.

The APA conditionally recommends:

Brief Eclectic Psychotherapy

Brief eclectic psychotherapy combines elements of cognitive behavioral therapy with a psychodynamic approach. It focuses on changing the emotions of shame and guilt and emphasizes the relationship between the patient and therapist. As conducted in research studies, treatment consists of 16 individual sessions, each lasting between 45 minutes and one hour. Sessions are typically scheduled once per week. Each of the 16 sessions has a specific objective. This intervention is intended for individuals who have experienced a single traumatic event.

Eye Movement Desensitization and Reprocessing (EMDR)

EMDR is a structured therapy developed by Francine Shapiro that encourages the patient to focus briefly on the trauma memory while simultaneously experiencing bilateral stimulation, which is associated with a reduction in the vividness and emotion associated with the trauma memories. The EMDR Institute describes the process as "unlike talk therapy, the insights clients gain in EMDR therapy result not so much from clinician interpretation but from the client's own accelerated intellectual and emotional processes." The past, present, and future are all addressed in an established eight-phase treatment process. EMDR is an individual therapy typically delivered one or two times per week for a total of six to twelve sessions. It differs from other trauma-focused treatments in that it does not include extended exposure to the distressing memory, detailed descriptions of the trauma, challenging of beliefs, or homework assignments.

Narrative Exposure Therapy (NET)

Narrative exposure therapy was developed for individuals who experienced trauma from ongoing war, conflict, and organized violence. It helps individuals establish a coherent life narrative in which to contextualize traumatic experiences. It is known for its use in group treatment for refugees.

Written Narrative Exposure

This therapy involves writing about the trauma during sessions and discussing with the provider any reactions to the writing assignment.

Medications

Currently, only the SSRIs (selective serotonin reuptake inhibitors) sertraline (Zoloft), and paroxetine (Paxil) are FDA-approved for the treatment of PTSD. While SSRIs are typically the first class of medications used in PTSD treatment, exceptions may occur for patients based upon their individual histories of side effects, responses, comorbidities, and personal preferences. SNRIs (serotonin-norepinephrine-reuptake inhibitors) are also used. Prazosin, an anti-hypertensive alpha-blocker has been used to treat nightmares.

OTHER THERAPIES

Brainspotting

Brainspotting is a relatively new form of therapy developed by former EMDR therapist David Grand (2013) that attempts to reprocess negative emotions by focusing on body-based sensations rather than thoughts. It encourages the client to be in control, with the therapist acting as the support. The processing is often performed using headphones and listening to bilaterally presented music (auditory bilateral stimulation). Like many other therapies, it treats trauma, anxiety, mental blocks, physical pain, and negative emotions.

Thought Field Therapy

A therapy developed by Roger Callahan (2001). Callahan theorizes that bodies consist of energy fields that when imbalanced cause physical and emotional problems. Focusing on an experience or thought associated with an emotional problem and "tapping" meridian points eliminates "blocks" and emotional upset. Some MHPs label Thought Field Therapy as pseudoscience, whereas others call for further study.

Emotional Freedom Technique

An alternative treatment developed by Gary Craig (2011) that is similar to thought field therapy in that it involves tapping meridian points or applying psychological acupressure to restore a balance in the body's energy system and relieve symptoms caused by a negative experience or emotion.

Traumatic Incident Reduction

TIR (Volkman, 2007) is a rapid (compared to traditional therapy) method of effectively reducing traumatic stress from emotionally and/or physically painful events in the past. It involves re-experiencing past traumas in a completely safe environment, free of distractions, judgments, or interpretation. TIR can be used as an adjunct to Critical Incident Stress Management (CISM).

IN HOUSE TREATMENT/TRAINING PROGRAMS

The On-Site Academy in Westminster, Massachusetts formed in 1992 offers CISM, substance/behavioral addiction and education, EMDR, TFT, IFS, group/individual debriefing, family support and education, law enforcement, firefighter, EMS, military veterans, sexual assault survivors, WINGS, LODI, and post-shoot as the first multiple-day treatment program specifically designed for first responders suffering from posttraumatic stress disorder/injuries.

In 2001, the **West Coast Posttrauma Retreat/The First Responder Support Network (WCPR)** modeled on the On-Site Academy, began in California. WCPR is for first responders whose lives have been impacted by their work experience. This six-day residential program provides education, support, and healing designed to help active, former, and retired first responders recognize the signs and symptoms of work-related stress, including posttraumatic stress injury (a.k.a.: posttraumatic stress disorder – PTSD) in themselves and in others. Satellite WCPR programs are being developed in other western and mid-western states. WCPR is part of the First Responders Support Network (https://www.frsn.org), which also includes the Significant Others and Spouses (SOS) program for the spouses or partners of first responders who have been affected by critical incidents (resulting in secondary or vicarious traumatization) experienced by their loved ones but may also be experiencing their own depression or anxiety symptoms and need to address their needs. In addition, these individuals may have their own trauma history, which is re-activated when his/her partner experiences a traumatic event.

First Responders Resiliency, Inc. is a nonprofit organization in Sonoma, California founded by former paramedic Susan Farren that is dedicated to training first responders to cope with the emotional trauma of their job. "First Responders Resiliency, Inc. addresses every component of the issues affecting first responders with the unique, multi-faceted approach of implementing education, skills, techniques, and tools that have profound impacts of stress reduction and management, thus improving the professional and personal lives of those that serve. The organization implements and leverages everything in their approach, from techniques used by the Navy Seals to the most recent research provided by neuroscientists and elite athletes alike."

As the awareness of the benefits of intensive outside help has increased, other short programs for first responders and the military have been developed, including 11th Hour Trauma Retreat, which utilizes EMDR for trauma reduction as well as other therapies such as attachment and relational therapy. In addition, treatment programs for civilians with PTSD/PTSI can be found in locations around the nation.

SELF-HELP

1. Resource installation (EMDR) includes using guided imagery and bilateral stimulation to create a safe place, access personal strengths, and create a trusted advisor. It is usually part of the EMDR protocol as part of therapy with an EMDR trained clinician but can be used independently between sessions to reduce triggers and promote relaxation.

2. Managing triggers includes learning to manage your environment, avoiding social media and excessive news, avoiding stimuli that trigger you, and having a safety plan for when you get triggered.

3. Relaxation

   There are many breathing exercises available to reduce para-sympathetic activity and increase parasympathetic response.

   Related activities also include mindfulness exercises and meditation, progressive muscle relaxation, self-soothing, and music therapy using earphones to access bilateral sound.

4. Integrative medicine approaches include Pilates, Acupuncture (VA approved), and Trauma Sensitive Yoga. The latter was developed by David Emerson and Bessel van der Kolk. This type of yoga focuses on gentle movements and has been shown to significantly reduce PTSD symptoms.

5. Social support includes online support groups such as PTSD Alliance and in-person support groups.

6. Journaling while focusing on the practice of gratitude is often helpful as are workbooks emphasizing exercises for PTSD symptom reduction and posttraumatic growth.

7. Additional treatments include virtual reality exposure, ketamine infusion and MDMA, hyperbaric oxygen therapy, and transcranial magnetic stimulation, which may be helpful while under the care of an experienced clinician (Tull, 2021). However, as of the writing of this book, these treatments do not have strong research behind them and should be discussed with a professional to determine the risks and benefits.

THE HERO'S JOURNEY FOR FIRST RESPONDERS

On their path from posttraumatic stress injury/disorder through recovery to posttraumatic growth, the first responders I treated over 40 years in practice, embarked on a psychic journey, different in each person, but similar in patterns and themes. The model I developed, based on the work of Chris Vogler (1998), is as follows.

Traveling from the ordinary civilian world to the world of first responders

When an individual leaves the ordinary civilian world to join the "extra" ordinary world of the first responder, he or she embarks on a journey into a netherworld, an underbelly of life outside the daily scope of the average person. In this new world, first responders are trained to override normal physical and psychological reactions; rather than running away from a fire or an armed suspect, the first responder is trained to pursue and overtake the threat. What would be a special world to another person becomes the ordinary world of the first responder, and the ego begins to perceive itself as different and separate from the rest of the human species.

Developing purpose and learning to adjust to and adapt to the "extraordinary" first responder world

Fictional heroes encourage the myth. Once our hero comes to believe that the world of the first responder is not accessible to the "sheep" in the civilian world, he or she accepts the myth of psychological and physical invulnerability. New recruits are raw ego and are eager to save the world with their newly acquired special skills. The true hero, who experiences strife, failure, and loss of control, learns from adversity, and can transcend the limits and fantasies of the ego to become a completely integrated human being.

Exposure to traumas, critical incidents, cumulative stress that leads to isolation, dysfunction, and psychological distress

As the first responder confronts new experiences over time, they can assimilate the information and reinforce their worldview. However, when an experience does not conform to the first responder's way of thinking, the manner in which they make sense of the world (e.g., if I do everything right, the call will turn out okay, people will appreciate me, I'm in control and will be a competent first responder, etc.) forces them into cognitive dissonance, or the psychological distress of holding two or more contradictory beliefs, values, or ideas in the mind simultaneously. If the call didn't go how I expected, what does that make me? Incompetent? Out of control? The first responder either must dismiss or suppress the experience (which may only last until another trigger bubbles up) or evolve to adapt to the new information and form a new meaning out of the situation by undergoing a tidal wave of cognitive and emotional change. In other words, the first responder no longer can grow quantitatively in their knowledge but is forced to make a qualitative leap into a new way of perceiving the world.

Loss of sense of purpose, vulnerability, the inability to continue as usual

Our hero's inner adventure begins after the hero has survived a significant event or events. On the surface, this may seem like the end of the story, but for our hero, it's the beginning. Our hero's ego has been challenged and the ability to cope is overwhelmed. Suddenly, an internal psychological world, full of ambiguities and open to interpretation, is "forced" upon the first responder. He or she can no longer remain in the comfort of the ordinary first responder world. Our hero's ability to survive psychologically, or physically, is at stake.

Refusal of the call to recovery followed by acceptance when there are no other options

The hero is about to face the greatest of all challenges: exploration of the self. This journey isn't routine or spontaneous. Fearful of the unknown, the first responder turns away from the challenge: "There's nothing wrong with me. I can handle it. I don't have the time. It's too much money. I can't take the time off work."

Some other change of circumstances or offense in the order of things—a threatened divorce, influence from a supervisor, the realization that a career is at stake, must take place to get the resident past the turning point. Once single or cumulative CIs have caused our Hero sufficient distress, secondary journey is forced upon them. The Responder may be surprised to learn that there's another world, previously hidden from their psyche that affects health, career, and life. Whereas the journeyman first responder has mastered the concrete, black and white world: us-them, dead-not dead, in custody-not in custody, the internal psychological world "forced" upon them is full of ambiguities and open to interpretation. Where formerly they had disparaged the idea of "touchy-feely, psycho-babble bullshit," they now must rely on it to save themselves.

Thus, our hero is presented with a challenge, problem, or critical incident that overwhelms the ability to cope. The horrible call or the series of events results in burnout, PTSD, Emergency Responder Exhaustion Syndrome, or other types of psychological distress. Confronted with devastating vulnerability, our hero can no longer remain in the comfort of their ordinary first responder world. A supervisor, a spouse, or a colleague realizes that the hero is in deep trouble and their very ability to survive emotionally, even physically, is at stake. To delay further would lead to even more tragedy. Unfortunately, sometimes our hero refuses the call until all is lost personally and professionally. Recovery is out of sight.

But if our hero accepts the call to adventure, there are internal obstacles and challenges to be overcome, including psychic wounds, grudges, spiritual and psychological doubts, fears, ignorance, failings, vices, dependencies, emotional scars, and self-limitations that inhibit growth and progress.

Viktor Frankl (2020) wrote, "Everything can be taken from a man but . . . the last of the human freedoms—to choose one's attitude in any given set of circumstances, to choose one's own way." Our hero must finally ask the question, "Do I want to live my life as I always have or risk everything for growth and change?" When a hero realizes that the options have run out and a choice must be made, they are propelled into the adventure. For some, the crossing is easy; others crash into the journey with a bang.

Finding friends, companions, allies, mentors for support along the journey

Companions, friends, allies, and mentors are helpers who can help our hero take off the "game face" and confront fears, secrets, and vulnerabilities. The mentor may be a peer who serves as a guide. This peer represents the bond between parent and child, teacher and student, doctor and patient, or God and man. Mentors who have experienced a psychic crisis of their own and gained wisdom are most helpful, and their encouragement can keep the hero from refusing the call. When peers disclose their vulnerability, confess secrets, and admit helplessness, and fear, our hero is given the gift of permission to acknowledge "weakness." In this way, interaction with the peer helps the hero let go of the shadow's power to control.

The mentor is a positive force who teaches, motivates, and protects the hero. Close connection with a candid, assertive mentor is essential to help our hero through the arduous search for self-identity and the will to turn away from dysfunctional, psychologically engulfing, work environments and/or families of origin. Mentors assist the hero in moving from passivity and sloth to becoming an active participant in emotional growth, overcoming psychic obstacles, and achieving real-life goals through the development of insight and wisdom.

Mentors, by necessity, must be enthused to do the job right. "Enthusiasm" stems from the Greek en Theos meaning, "god inspired, having a god within you, or in the presence of a god" (Vogler, 1998).

Defending against Obstacles and Self-sabotage

Once our hero accepts the call to adventure, the journey begins. Our hero begins to confront external forces (family, the department) that don't want our hero to break away from the dysfunctional system. Along the way, internal forces, such as the unconscious "shadow," or dark side of the personality, appear. Our hero would rather charge into a burning building or confront a perpetrator holding a loaded rifle than face the inner monsters of emotions, vulnerabilities, secrets, and fears. As perceived by the hero, the shadow is the enemy made up of inner demons, fears, angers, and suppressed emotions that the ER-hero is terrified to face.

Our hero may forcefully resist bringing the shadow into consciousness because it represents perceived inferiority, weakness, helplessness, and characteristics of someone who is not worthy of being a first responder. Often, the first responder projects perceived their deficiencies onto others, i.e., the wife, the command staff, or the world, which serves to isolate them even more from potentially supportive people. However, if the ravages of unresolved trauma are to be overcome, a separation from these forces is essential.

Peers have a unique perspective into the inner workings behind the game face because, as wounded mentors, they've "been there" themselves and can call the hero on their bullshit.

Confronting addictions, isolation, anger, depression, anxiety

Many first responders have learned to cope with their troubles by using alcohol, gambling, affairs, and other self-destructive behaviors.

The ordeal or the figurative death of the false self and discovery of the true self

On the journey, our hero endures an ordeal of the spirit. He or she hits bottom emotionally and faces the death of entrenched but inadequate defense mechanisms and self-defeating behaviors. In this challenging, yet critical part, our hero faces and confronts the shadow, which may appear in the form of cynicism. The resistance to the work is frequently the greatest source of strength as the Shadow is transformed from weakness and vulnerability into acceptable and necessary human qualities of compassion and sensitivity. Amazingly, as the hero progresses, the shadow is reframed into a positive, creative force. The shadow is accepted as a core of healthy, natural emotions that our hero has been trained to suppress, repress, or forget.

A problem-focused coping style is related to higher posttraumatic growth (PTG), especially positive thinking. Individuals who try to learn from difficulties report highest PTG. Emotion-focused coping is related to PTG in individuals frequently exposed to traumatic experiences in their work environment. Rumination and self-blaming may be maladaptive in the face of everyday situations but may result in growth when used by first responders, who have frequent exposure to trauma. Intrusive thoughts, in the form of repetitive purposeful thoughts focused on aspects of the struggle, indicate cognitive processing and may be a useful strategy and adaption to working through the experience. This is different from ruminating on negative, unwanted thoughts. Self-blame can be useful if the result is changing the perception of the self or others involved in the incident. (Rodriguez-Rey et al, 2017)

Looking backward: vulnerabilities that triggered the reaction to the critical incident

Betrayal or abandonment is a major obstacle to progressing in the career or life. The damage from betrayal to a first responder cannot be understated and leaves the perception of total defeat, and the anger and helplessness. Many first responders have experienced some form of betrayal or abandonment, first by narcissistic, absent, or alcoholic parents, and later (at least in their perception) by supervisors. Many heroes come from a family in which there was a cold, distant father and an absent or non-nurturing mother. Hence, they enter the emergency services injured already.

The positive aspect of surviving a dysfunctional childhood is that our hero can adapt easily to a dysfunctional job environment because the coping mechanisms they developed in childhood tend to give them greater concern for social issues and a deep need to "make a difference." Without reconciliation, hostility and fear come raging back and may unconsciously trigger a reaction to a critical event. Through "hard wiring," our hero's dysfunctional view of the world sets up the dynamics leading to maladaptive responses to the CIs.

The experience of revelation, "connecting the dots" leads to transformation and resurrection. When our heroes gain the knowledge that they were able to survive their deepest anxieties and terrors, they can return to the ordinary world of work and family with an elixir of insight and wisdom. Gaining knowledge that their skill, willingness, and ability to face the ultimate adversity and overcome it is transformative for the first responder. This ordeal has also given our hero a better understanding of how others were damaged and unable to fulfill their parental or caretaker duties. The ultimate goal is to "let go" of the chains of disappointment, hurt, rejection, and anger that have held them captive by the people who let them down.

Seizing the sword of self-knowledge: coping with triggers

Having survived the death of soul-defeating defenses, The "sword" is knowledge and experience, greater understanding, and reconciliation with the hostile forces of ignorance, shame, and guilt. The journey is not yet over. The first responder must learn to cope with, manage, and understand their specific triggers. Otherwise, they will be stuck in a state of anxiety that a trigger will appear, and they will be projected right back into the scary, out-of-control place.

The first step in dealing with triggers is to accept that they will occur. Fighting being triggered only gives the trigger more power. For example, if I tell a client, "Don't think about pink elephants. Whatever you do, don't think about pink elephants," then what is the client thinking about? However, I could also say, "You'll think about pink elephants now and again, but if you allow yourself to experience thinking about pink elephants, the thought will eventually be replaced by some other thought." The second statement reduces the power of thinking about pink elephants because trying not to think about, experience, or feel about something puts the person's full attention on it.

The next step is to label the emotional reaction. Do pink elephants make me scared? Angry? Helpless? The point is that trying to deny the emotion is futile because it's still present. Labeling it takes away its power to control.

Third, listen to your body to determine what triggered the emotion, thought, and reaction. Does your gut tighten, heart rate increase, breathing become shallow? When has that happened before? For example, was it when your father yelled at you and humiliated you in front of your friends? And your commander has done the same thing in front of your co-workers? The dots are connected. You react to your commander the same way you did your father.

Now you can decide what to do. Do you want to allow your commander to make you feel like a small child? Or do choose to not allow him into your head and heart. This is called "not taking it personally." In other words, understand that your commander's reactions are because of his perceptions, or because he had a fight with his wife, or whatever. He may be angry with you, but that's his problem, not yours.

Finally, be willing to be less controlling over your emotions and thoughts. They will come and go. Some will be upsetting until you figure out your triggers. Let your negative feelings about your negative feelings go. Fear of your thoughts and emotions is paralyzing. You can choose to think or feel something else.

Returning to the community (the road back)

The first responder recommits to the journey and accepts the return to the ordinary world. They haven't moved laterally and learned only a new way of dealing with reactions, but also have gained wisdom vertically and perceive inevitable problems as a chance to grow and gain more self-knowledge. If these ideas are presented as a journey, inevitable future struggles in life rather than roadblocks. This fits into the first responder's natural propensity to be autonomous and capable of solving problems, but on an entirely new level. The hero experiences posttraumatic growth as defined by Tedeschi and Calhoun (2004) in that they develop improved relationships, new possibilities for one's life, a greater appreciation for life, and a greater sense of personal strength and spiritual development. Ultimately, their losses have produced valuable gains.

Return with the elixir: giving back to other first responders

The journey is meaningless unless the hero brings back the elixir—a magic potion with the power to heal. Without the elixir, the ER-hero is doomed to repeat the journey until the issues are resolved. Our healthy heroes come to understand that their own recovery depends on their willingness to mentor others through modeling, counseling, or offering support. Some first responders have gone on to earn degrees and become MHP, thus giving them a unique understanding of the culture and psychological needs of first responders.

APPENDIX B

RURAL POLICING

Most police agencies across the nation are not in metropolitan areas, but small or rural towns. According to the U.S. Census Bureau (2016), 97% of the United States' land mass is rural. About one-fifth of the population, 60 million people, inhabit rural areas. Many are employed in agriculture, forestry, mining, and manufacturing, sectors that are plagued by declining job opportunities. Rural areas are often characterized by conservative values, aversion to government interference and authority, a tendency to exert social control among their own, and higher gun ownership than urban areas.

In 2013, 71% of all police departments served jurisdictions of fewer than 10,000 residents, and 30% served communities of less than 2,500 residents. About half of law enforcement departments have fewer than ten officers (Weisner et al., 2020).

Rural agencies lack the tax base to fund social programs, including police and public safety. They are underfunded, understaffed, and lack training opportunities and necessary equipment, resources, and technology. Rural police departments not only have access to fewer resources than urban departments, but their jurisdictions are also characterized by large geographical areas and hours-long response times. Rural police officers also face growing pressure to cover even more territory, respond to more service calls, deal with more violent crime, and more sophisticated criminals. The rise of illicit drugs, including manufacturing labs, grows, and distribution, leads to violence, death, and disruption in families and the community. As a result, rural officers are increasingly called upon to manage homelessness, drug addiction, and mental illness, social problems for which they may receive inadequate training and have insufficient resources funding, equipment, and technology. Adequate mental health facilities have limited funding and have often gone by the wayside requiring peace officers to potentially use law enforcement tactics on individuals who need psychiatric care. Jails become overcrowded, and prosecution seems pointless.

Consequently, big-city solutions to policing issues are often not relevant to small-town and rural police departments. A sheriff's deputy explains, "In rural policing, we see and touch it all. Any of us could be first on scene at a traffic collision or a homicide. We're search and rescue, the coroner, the victim advocate at the scene of domestic violence, the family therapist, the sex crimes investigator, and the ones who evacuate people from wildfires."

With few resources and more area and responsibilities to cover, rural officers are spread thin and face mental health issues secondary to psychological stress that may be exacerbated by isolation, cultural barriers, geographical location, and limited access to mental health professionals. According to the National Police Foundation, 2020, small communities are overwhelmed. Because rural departments have a unique culture, they necessarily develop their own methods of doing things depending on local history, demographics, size, and budget. (Wooley & Smith, 2022)

REFERENCES

Aanenson, Q. C. (1993). *A fighter pilot's story*. Documentary.

Andrew, S. (August 26, 2020). *Why police shoot so many times to bring down a suspect*. CNN. https://www.cnn.com/2020/08/26/us/why-police-shoot-so-many-rounds-trnd/index.html

American Psychiatric Association. (2013). *Diagnostic and statistical manual of mental disorders (5th ed.)*. Arlington, VA: Author.

American Psychological Association (2020). *PTSD Treatments*. https://www.apa.org/ptsd-guideline/treatments

Calhoun, L.G., Tedeschi, R.G (2013). *Posttraumatic growth in clinical practice*. Routledge/Taylor & Francis Group.

Callahan, R. J. (2001). *Tapping the healer within: Using thought-field therapy to instantly conquer your fears, anxieties, and emotional distress*. New York: McGraw-Hill Education.

Cameron, C. (2022, June 13) These are the people who died in connection with the Capitol Riot. NYTimes. https://www.nytimes.com/2022/01/05/us/politics/jan-6-capitol-deaths.html

Campbell, J. (1973). *The hero with a thousand faces*. Princeton University Press.

Campbell, J. (1991). *The power of myth*. Anchor.

Cappucci, M. (2018, November 14). California's Carr fire spawned a true fire tornado. *Science News for Students*. Retrieved from https://www.sciencenewsforstudents.org/article/californias-carr-fire-spawned-true-fire-tornado.

Charoen, Patrick P., "Officer involved shooting: The emotional impact and the effective coping strategies" (1999). UNLV Theses, Dissertations, Professional Papers, and Capstones. 288. http://dx.doi.org/10.34917/1481139

Craig, G. (2011). *The EFT Manual. 2nd edition.* Energy Psychology Press. 2nd edition.

Frankl, V. E. (2020). *Man's search for meaning.* Rider Books.

Freyd, J. (1994). Betrayal trauma: Traumatic amnesia as an adaptive response to childhood abuse. Ethics & Behavior, 4(4), 307–329. https://doi.org/10.1207/s15327019eb0404_1

Grand, D. (2013). *Brainspotting: The revolutionary new therapy for rapid and effective change.* Sounds True.

Grossman, D. (1996) *On killing: The psychological cost of learning to kill in war and society.* New York: Little, Brown and Company.

International Association of Chiefs of Police. (2016). *Officer-Involved Shootings: A guide for law enforcement leaders.* Washington, D.C. Office of Community Oriented Policing Services. https://www.theiacp.org/sites/default/files/2018-08/e051602754_Officer_Involved_v8.pdf

Jinkerson, J.D. (2016). Defining and assessing moral injury: A syndrome perspective. *Traumatology,* 22(2), 122-130. http://dx.doi.org/10.1037/trm0000069

Frankl, V. E. (2020). *Man's search for meaning.* Rider Books.

Foskett, J. (2020). Q&A: Understanding PTSD and PTSI in the fire service. *FireRescue1,* June 8, 2020. https://www.firerescue1.com/ptsd/articles/qa-understanding-ptsd-and-ptsi-in-the-fire-service-Xgf61nj1N4oKf0Ka/

Katz, J. (1995, May 24). COLUMN ONE: A Hero's Fame Leads to Tragedy: Helping to pull little Jessica McClure from a Texas well made firefighter Robert O'Donnell a star. But the limelight soon turned to darkness. http://articles.latimes.com/1995-05-24/news/mn-5474_1_jessica-mcclure. *Los Angeles Times.* https://www.latimes.com/archives/la-xpm-1995-05-24-mn-5474-story.html.

Kirschman, E., Kamena, M. & Fay, J. (2014) *Counseling cops: What clinicians need to know.* New York: Guilford Press. 70-72.

LeDoux, J. E. (1996). *The emotional brain: The mysterious underpinnings of emotional life.* Simon & Schuster.

Lewis-Schroeder, N. F., Kieran, K., Murphy, B.L., Wolff, J. D., Robinson, M. A. & Kaufman, M. L. (July-August 2018) Conceptualization, assessment, and treatment of traumatic stress in first responders: A review of critical issues. *Harvard Review of Psychiatry,* 26(4): 216-227. https://www.ncbi.nlm.nih.gov/pmc/articles/PMC6624844/

Luskin, F. (2010) *Forgive for good: A proven prescription for health and happiness.* San Francisco: HarperOne.

Mitchell, J.T. (1983). When disaster strikes: The critical incident stress debriefing process. *Journal of Emergency Medical Services, 8,* 35-39.

Mitchell, J. T. (2020). Critical Incident Stress Management: A Comprehensive, Integrative, Systematic, and Multi-Component Program for Supporting First Responder Psychological Health. In C. Bowers, D. Beidel, & M. Marks (Eds.), *Mental Health Intervention and Treatment of First Responders and Emergency Workers* (pp. 103-128). IGI Global. http://doi:10.4018/978-1-5225-9803-9.ch007

Mitchell, J.T. & Everly, G.S. Jr., (2001). *Critical incident stress debriefing: An operations manual for CISD, defusing and other group crisis intervention services (3rd ed.).* Ellicott City, Md.: Chevron Publishing Corporation.

National Center for PTSD. (2021). U.S. Department of Veterans Affairs. https://www.ptsd.va.gov/index.asp

National Police Foundation. (2020). *Conversations with Rural Law Enforcement Leaders: Volume 1.* https://cops.usdoj.gov/RIC/Publications/cops-w0892-pub.pdf

Orrick, D. (April 18, 2022). Can suicide be 'in the line of duty?' Police officer's widow, lawmakers hope to change the rules. *Police 1. https://www.police1. com/lodd/articles/can-suicide-be-in-the-line-of-duty-police-officers-widow-lawmakers-hope-to-change-the-rules-Y5FdAgIqW5al2ok4/*

Pace-Schott, E., Germain, A., & Milad, M. (2015). Sleep and REM sleep disturbance in the pathophysiology of PTSD: the role of extinction memory. *Biology of Mood & Anxiety Disorders.* https://www.ncbi.nlm.nih.gov/pmc/articles/PMC4450835/

Papazouglou, K., Bonanno, G., Blumberg, D., & Keesee, T. (September 10, 2019). *Moral Injury in Police Work.* LEB. https://leb.fbi.gov/articles/featured-articles/moral-injury-in-police-work

Police 1. (April 13, 2020). *Why 911 dispatchers should be considered first responders.* https://www.police1.com/police-products/police-technology/publicsafetysoftware/articles/why-911-dispatchers-should-be-considered-first-responders-V0H4cmLgYnP47ntK/.

Rodríguez-Rey, R., Palacios, A., Alonso-Tapia, J., Pérez, E., Álvarez, E., Coca, A., Mencía, S., Marcos, A. M., Mayordomo-Colunga, J., Fernández, F., Gómez, F., Cruz, J., Barón, L., Calderón, R. M., & Belda, S. (2017). Posttraumatic growth in pediatric intensive care personnel: Dependence on resilience and coping strategies. *Psychological Trauma: Theory, Research, Practice, and Policy, 9*(4), 407–415. https://doi.org/10.1037/tra0000211

Shapiro, F. (2017) *Eye movement desensitization and reprocessing (EMDR) therapy: Basic principles, protocols, and procedures. 3rd edition.* The Guilford Press.

Skeffington, P. (2021, February 4). One in five police officers are at risk or PTSD—here's how we need to respond. *The Conversation.* http://theconversation.

com/one-in-five-police-officers-are-at-risk-of-ptsd-heres-how-we-need-to-respond-63272.

Solomon, Roger (2011). Critical incident trauma for law enforcement officers. Cited in Moad, C. (2011). *Critical Incidents: Responding to Police Officer Trauma.* Criminal Justice Institute.

Spence, D.L. & Drake, J. (2021). *Law enforcement suicide: 2020 report to Congress.* Washington, D.C.: U.S. Department of Justice.

Sullivan, R. & Lasley, E. (2010) *Fear in Love: Attachment, abuse, and the developing brain.* Cerebrum: Dana Foundation. https://www.dana.org/article/fear-in-love/

Tedeschi, R.G. & Calhoun, L.G. (2004). Posttraumatic growth: A new perspective on psychotraumatology. *Psychiatric Times.* XXI (4). Retrieved from http://www.psychiatrictimes.com/p040458.html

Tedeschi, R.G. & Moore, B.A. (2016). *The posttraumatic growth workbook: coming through trauma wiser, stronger, and more resilient.* New Harbinger.

Terr, L. (1992) *Too scared to cry: Psychic trauma in childhood.* Basic Books.

The Sobering Truth. badge of life. (n.d.). https://policesuicide.spcollege.edu/assets/BadgeofLife_July2016.pdf.

Tiesman, H.M., Elkins, K.L., Brown, M., Marsh, S. & Carson, L.M. (April 6, 2021) *Suicides among first responders: A call to action.* NIOSH Science Blog. Centers for Disease Control and Prevention. https://blogs.cdc.gov/niosh-science-blog/2021/04/06/suicides-first-responders

Tucker, E., & Krishnakumar, P. (January 13, 2022) Intentional killings of law enforcement officers reach a 20-year high, FBI says. *CNN. https://www.cnn.com/2022/01/13/us/police-officers-line-of-duty-deaths/index.html*

Tull, M. (2020). Development of PTSD in firefighters. Verywellmind. https://www.verywell.com/rates-of-ptsd-in-firefighters-2797428

Tull, M. (2021) How PTSD is treated. Verywellmind. https://www.verywellmind.com/ptsd-treatment-2797659

U.S. Census Bureau (2016). New census data shows differences between urban and rural populations. https://www.census.gov/newsroom/press-releases/2016/cb16-210.html

Van der Kolk B. & Fisler R. (1995). Dissociation and the fragmentary nature of traumatic memories: overview and exploratory study. *J Trauma Stress,* Oct;8(4):505-25. doi: 10.1007/BF02102887. PMID: 8564271.

Van der Kolk, B. (2014). *The body keeps the score: Brain, mind, and body in the healing of trauma.* N.Y., N.Y.: Penguin Books.

Venteicher, Wes. (2017, March 19). Increasing suicide rates among first responders spark concern. *FireRescue1.* https://www.firerescue1.com/fire-ems/

articles/increasing-suicide-rates-among-first-responders-spark-concern-TkuBikGnO3vPHIb3/.

Violanti, J.M. & Aron, F. (1995). Police stressors: Variations in perception among police personnel. *Journal of Criminal Justice, 23*(3), 287-294. https://doi.org/10.1016/0047-2352(95)00012-F

Vogler, C., (1998). *The writer's journey: Mythic structure for writers (2nd ed.).* Studio City, CA: Michael Wiese Productions.

Weisner, L., Otto, H. D., & Adams, S. (2020). Issues in Policing Rural Areas: A Review of the Literature. *Criminal Justice Information Authority.* https://doi.org/10.13140/RG.2.2.10290.76489

Wolfe, J. (2021, August 2). Four officers who responded to U.S. Capitol attack have died by suicide. *Reuters. https://www.reuters.com/world/us/officer-who-responded-us-capitol-attack-is-third-die-by-suicide-2021-08-02/*

Wooley, M.J., Powell, S., & Loew, M. (December 2019). How to survive a firestorm and empower more resilient wildland firefighters. *Crisis, Stress, and Human Resilience. 1*(3), 171-182.

Wooley, M.J. & Smith, S. (June 2022). Reaching Rural Police: Challenges, Implications, and Applications. *Crisis, Stress, and Human Resilience. 4*(1), 65-83.

ADDITIONAL RESOURCES AND READING

"About Blue H.E.L.P.,". https://bluehelp.org/about-us/.

Anthony, Kiara. (September 18, 2018). EFT Tapping. Healthline. https://www.healthline.com/health/eft-tapping

Bauer, A.L., & Toman, S. (2003). A Gestalt Perspective of Crisis Debriefing: Working in the Here and Now When the Here and Now is Unbearable. *Gestalt Review*, 7 (1): 56-71.

Bohl, N. (1995). Professionally administered critical incident debriefing for police officers: In M.I. Kunke & E.M. Scrivner (Eds.), *Police Psychology into the 21st century* (pp. 169-188). Hillsdale: Erlbaum.

Calhoun L.G., & Tedeschi R.G. (1998). Posttraumatic growth: future directions. In R.G. Tedeschi, C.L. Park, L.G. Calhoun (Eds.), *Posttraumatic Growth: Positive Changes in the Aftermath of Crisis* (pp. 215-238). Mahwah, N.J.: Lawrence Erlbaum Associates Publishers.

Calhoun, L.G., Tedeschi, R.G. (1999). *Facilitating Posttraumatic Growth: A Clinician's Guide.* Mahwah, N.J.: Lawrence Erlbaum Associates Publishers.

Cohen, A. (2002). Gestalt therapy and Post-Traumatic Stress Disorder: The potential and its (lack of) fulfillment. *Gestalt,* 6:1-11. Retrieved July 15, 2002. http://www.g.gorg.gej.6-1

Everly, G.S., & Mitchell, J.T. (1997) *A Primer on Critical Incident Stress Management (CISM). The International Critical Incident Stress Foundation.* www.icisf.org/about/cismprimer.pdf

Harvard Health Publishing (July 6, 2020) Understanding the stress response. *Harvard Medical School.*

McAdams, D.P. (1997). *The stories we live by: Personal myths and the making of the self.* New York: Guilford Press.

Lawson, Gerard. (2005). The Hero's journey as a developmental metaphor in counseling. *Journal of Humanistic Counseling, Education and Development.* Fall 2005, 134-144. link.galegroup.com/apps/doc/A139299061/SUIC?u=pennhs& xid=232aee4d. Accessed 24 Feb. 2017.

Mitchell, J.T. (2003), Crisis intervention & CISM: a research summary. Retrieved February 11, 2004, from www.icisf.org/articles/cism_research_summary.pdf

Mitchell, J.T. & Everly, G. (2000). Critical incident stress debriefing: Evolutions, effects, and outcomes. In B. Raphael & J.P. Wilson (Eds.), *Stress debriefing: Theory, practice, and challenge* (71-90). London: Cambridge University Press.

National Wildfire Coordinating Group. November 19, 2020. https://www.nwcg.gov/positions/fban

Sapolsky, R.M. (2017). *Behave.* Penguin Books.

Shumake, K. (July 2019) *The benefits of self-forgiveness.* BeWell Stanford https://bewell.stanford.edu/the-benefits-of-self-forgiveness/

Tedeschi, R.G. & Calhoun, L.G. (1995). *Trauma & transformation: Growing in the aftermath of suffering.* Thousand Oaks, Calif.: Sage Publications.

Tedeschi, R.G. & Calhoun, L.G. (1996) The Posttraumatic Growth Inventory: Measuring the positive legacy of trauma. *Journal of Traumatic Stress.* 9(3), 455-471.

ACKNOWLEDGMENTS

I could have not written this book without the honesty and vulnerability of the first responders who unselfishly and heroically chose to share stories of the most personal and traumatic events in their lives. I am truly honored and humbled that they placed their trust in me. There were many other stories I would have liked to include, but the project had to conclude at some point. Each and every one of the individuals who contributed is a gift to my heart.

I also thank my readers and advisors for their patience and tolerance and brilliance. I'm not an easy taskmaster. Thanks to Leslie Gabriele, Sharon Smith, Sharon Owen, Jessica Wooley, Lou Zimmer, Shaneika Smith, and Howard VanEs of Let's Write Books, Inc. for publishing services. Over the years my colleagues and friends at the West Coast Posttrauma Retreat and First Responders Support Network have offered me invaluable suggestions and support for this project. I am indebted to you all.

ABOUT THE AUTHOR

Marilyn Wooley is a police and public safety psychologist and traumatologist who has provided treatment to cops, firefighters, communications dispatchers, medical personnel, other first responders, and veterans suffering from posttraumatic stress injuries for the past forty years. She completed her PhD in 1977 from the University of Arizona and performed her postdoctoral training at the Long Beach Veterans Medical Center treating veterans injured and traumatized during the Vietnam War. Her experiences spurred her interest in the development and treatment of posttraumatic stress.

Marilyn Wooley

Marilyn's passion became even more deeply rooted when, in 1992, she discovered a trunk filled with her grandfather's effects from WWII. By exploring hundreds of his letters and photographs, she discovered that her grandfather had served in the 7th Army and was a liberator of Dachau Prison Camp. Suddenly, she realized that her grandfather's gruesome experiences had left him suffering from untreated posttraumatic stress disorder and her interest in PTSD became an obsession. The diaries illuminated Wooley's troubled family history and she was struck with fresh clarity how her clients' individual experiences with posttraumatic stress not only shaped their lives but influenced and shaped the lives of their families and children. Her therapeutic goal of reducing the effects of PTSD eventually led her to devote her energy to helping first responders embark on a journey from posttraumatic stress to recovery to posttraumatic growth that would ultimately reclaim and enrich their lives.

Wooley began private practice in Redding, California in 1979. Over the years she sought opportunities to gain experience in the treatment of posttraumatic stress and related disorders. She became an instructor in Critical Incident Stress Management education and provided services to numerous law enforcement, fire, emergency medical services, government agencies, private companies, and medical facilities.

In her work, she witnessed the positive changes associated with posttraumatic growth in hundreds of first responders. Over time, she recognized a pattern similar to the Hero's Journey archetype in classic mythology described by Joseph Campbell, and she took classes detailing the Writer's Journey developed by screenwriter/author Chris Vogler. Her conceptualization of the "hero's story" helped her understand her clients' struggles. When she began to share this story with the first responders she treated, they began to see their recovery as an adventure, not the one they experience in their daily life, but a journey inside, both terrifying and inspirational. Posttraumatic growth, when described as a series of challenges, becomes normalized and helps the first responder negotiate the path to recovery in a more understandable way.

Wooley has published articles in professional journals and presented papers at conferences describing critical incidents, including her own, and the coping/recovery process. She is an expert witness in several areas relating to trauma. She volunteered for the American Red Cross to help victims of 9/11. She has also volunteered as a clinician for the West Coast Posttrauma Retreat since 2001 and served on the board of the First Responders Support Network.

Writing about PTSD is not Wooley's only genre. She won the St. Martin's Press Best First Novel award for *Jackpot Justice,* which was published in 2000. *Jackpot Justice* is the story of fictional psychologist, Cassie Ringwald, who lives amid colorful characters and solves mysteries to save the lives of her clients.

Wooley lives in rural Northern California with her husband and clowder of shameless cats. She enjoys an adrenaline rush and has survived skydiving over power lines, flying a small plane crippled by engine icing, scuba diving with sharks, kayaking 100 miles on Idaho's "River of No Return", and belly dancing in a biker bar. She also tends to her rose garden and attends opera whenever she can. She is hooked on murder mysteries, history, and world travel.

Printed in Great Britain
by Amazon

16776366R00129